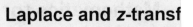

Laplace and z-transf

Mathematics for Engineers

The series is designed to provide engineering students in colleges and universities with a mathematical toolkit, each book including the mathematics in an engineering context. Numerous worked examples, and problems with answers, are included.

1. Laplace and z-transforms

Titles in production

2. Ordinary differential equations
3. Complex numbers
4. Fourier series

Mathematics for Engineers

Laplace and z-transforms

W.Bolton

Longman
Scientific &
Technical

Longman Scientific & Technical,
Longman Group UK Limited,
Longman House, Burnt Mill, Harlow,
Essex, CM20 2JE, England
and Associated Companies throughout the world.

First published 1994

ISBN 0 582 228190

Printed in Malaysia by TCP

British Library Cataloguing in Publication Data
A CIP record for this book is available from the British Library

Contents

Preface vii

1   The Laplace transform 1
1.1 The Laplace transform 1
1.2 The Laplace transform from first principles 3
1.3 The unit step function 4
1.4 Impulse function 9
1.5 Standard Laplace transforms 11
1.6 Properties of Laplace transforms 14
Further problems 21

2   Inverse Laplace transform 23
2.1 The inverse transform 23
2.2 Partial fractions 25
2.3 Using Laplace transform properties 31
2.4 Convolution theorem 33
Further problems 34

3   Transform of derivatives and integrals 35
3.1 The transform of derivatives 35
3.2 The transform of integrals 38
3.3 Solving differential equations 40
3.4 Simultaneous differential equations 46
3.5 Initial and final value theorems 49
Further problems 52

4   Electrical circuits in the s-domain 56
4.1 Circuit elements in the s-domain 56
4.2 Circuits in the s-domain 61
Further problems 70

5   System transfer functions 73
5.1 The transfer function 73
5.2 Systems in series 79
5.3 Systems with feedback loops 80
5.4 Poles and zeros 82
Further problems 87

6   Sampled data systems and *z*-transforms 92
6.1 Sampled data systems 92
6.2 The *z*-transform 95
6.3 Standard *z*-transforms 98
6.4 Properties of the *z*-transform 101
6.5 The inverse *z*-transform 106
Further problems 108

7   The *z*-transfer function 110
7.1 Discrete transfer function 110
7.2 Zero-order-hold 114
Further problems 116

Answers to problems 119

Index 128

Preface

This is one of the books in a series designed to provide engineering students in colleges and universities with a mathematical toolkit. In the United Kingdom it is aimed primarily at HNC/HND students and first-year undergraduates. Thus the mathematics assumed is that in BTEC National Certificates and Diplomas or in A level. The pace of development of the mathematics has been aimed at the notional reader for whom mathematics is not their prime interest or "best subject" but need the mathematics in their other studies. The mathematics is developed and applied in an engineering context with large numbers of worked examples and problems, all with answers, being supplied.

This book is concerned with Laplace and z-transforms and their application in, primarily, electrical/electronic and control engineering. A familiarity with basic calculus is assumed. The aim has been to include sufficient worked examples and problems to enable the reader to acquire some proficiency in the handling of Laplace transforms and an introduction to z-transforms.

W.Bolton

1 The Laplace transform

1.1 The Laplace transform

In engineering and science there are many relationships which give a relation between the rates of change of quantities, rather than between the quantities themselves. The derivative of a function represents a rate of change and an equation involving derivatives is called a *differential equation*. For example, when a source of voltage V is connected to a circuit containing a capacitor and resistor then the potential difference across the capacitor v_C is related to time t by the differential equation

$$V = RC \frac{dv_C}{dt} + v_C$$

There are a number of ways of solving such an equation and ending up with an equation involving just v_C and t, with no rates of change, i.e.

$$v_C = V(1 - e^{-t/RC})$$

One method by which this, and differential equations in general, can be solved is the *Laplace transform*.

Differential equations that describe how systems, such as an electrical circuit, behave with time are transformed by means of the Laplace transform into simple algebraic relationships, not involving time, where we can carry out normal algebraic manipulations of the quantities. We talk of the circuit behaviour in the *time domain* being transformed to the *s-domain*. Then we use an inverse transform to obtain the solution describing how a signal varies with time, i.e. transform from the *s*-domain back to the time domain.

1.1.1 Definition of the Laplace transform

Consider a quantity which is a function of time; we can talk of this quantity being in the *time domain*. We can represent such a function as $f(t)$. In many problems we are only concerned with values of time greater than or equal to 0, i.e. $t \geq 0$. To obtain the Laplace transform of this function we multiply it by e^{-st} and then integrate with respect to time from zero to infinity. Here s is a constant with the unit of 1/time. The result is what we now call the *Laplace transform* and the equation is then said to be in the s-domain. Thus the Laplace transform of the function of time $f(t)$ is

$$\mathcal{L}\{f(t)\} = \int_0^\infty e^{-st} f(t) \mathrm{d}t \qquad [1]$$

The transform is *one-sided* in that values are only considered between 0 and $+\infty$, and not over the full range of time from $-\infty$ to $+\infty$.

We can then carry out algebraic manipulations on the quantity in the s-domain, i.e. we can add, subtract, divide and multiply in the normal way we can with any algebraic quantities. We could not have done this on the original function, assuming it to be in the form of a differential equation, when in the time domain. By this means we can obtain a considerably simplified expression in the s-domain. When we want to see how the quantity varies with time in the time domain then we have to carry out the inverse transformation. This involves finding out what time domain function could have given the simplified s-domain expression.

A function of time is written as $f(t)$. A special symbol $\mathcal{L}$, called the *Laplace operator*, is commonly used to indicate the operation of making the transform. Thus $\mathcal{L}\{f(t)\}$ indicates that the Laplace transform is being taken of $f(t)$ to give the function in the s-domain. When in the s-domain a function is usually written, since it is a function of s, as $F(s)$. It is usual to use a capital letter F for the Laplace transform and a lower-case letter f for the time-varying function $f(t)$. Thus

$$\mathcal{L}\{f(t)\} = F(s) \qquad [2]$$

For the inverse operation when the function of time is obtained from the Laplace transform we can write

$$f(t) = \mathcal{L}^{-1}\{F(s)\} \qquad [3]$$

This equation thus reads as: $f(t)$ is the inverse transform of the Laplace transform $F(s)$.

1.2 The Laplace transform from first principles

To illustrate the transformation of a quantity from the time domain into the s-domain, consider a function that has the constant value of 1 for all values of time greater than 0, i.e. $f(t) = 1$ for $t \geq 0$. The Laplace transform is then, using equation [1],

$$\mathcal{L}\{f(t)\} = F(s) = \int_0^\infty 1\,e^{-st}\,dt = -\frac{1}{s}[e^{-st}]_0^\infty$$

Since with $t = \infty$ the value of e is 0 and with $t = 0$ the value of e^{-0} is -1, then

$$F(s) = \frac{1}{s} \tag{4}$$

Now consider the Laplace transform of the function $f(t) = a$, where a is a constant for all values of t greater than 0.

$$F(s) = \int_0^\infty a\,e^{-st}\,dt = a\int_0^\infty e^{-st}\,dt = \frac{a}{s} \tag{5}$$

This is just a multiplied by the transform of the function $f(t) = 1$, i.e. equation [4]. The multiplication of some function of time by a constant a gives a Laplace transform which is just the multiplication of the Laplace transform of that function by the constant.

Example

Determine, from first principles, the Laplace transform of the function e^{at}, where a is a constant.

The Laplace transform of this function $f(t) = e^{at}$ is thus

$$F(s) = \int_0^\infty e^{at}e^{-st}\,dt$$

$$= \int_0^\infty e^{-(s-a)t}\,dt = -\frac{1}{s-a}[e^{-(s-a)t}]_0^\infty$$

When $t = \infty$ then the term in the brackets becomes 0 and when $t = 0$ it becomes -1. Thus

$$F(s) = \frac{1}{s-a} \tag{6}$$

Example

Determine from first principles the Laplace transform of the function $f(t) = t^3$.

$$F(s) = \int_0^\infty e^{-st}t^3\,dt$$

This can be solved by using integration by parts, i.e.

$$\int u \, dv = uv - \int v \, du$$

with $dv = e^{-st}$ and $u = t^3$. Thus

$$F(s) = \left[\frac{t^3 e^{-st}}{-s} \right]_0^{\infty} - \int_0^{\infty} \frac{3t^2 e^{-st}}{-s} \, dt$$

This integral can then have integration by parts applied to it, with $dv = e^{-st}$ and $u = t^2$.

$$F(s) = \left[\frac{t^3 e^{-st}}{-s} \right]_0^{\infty} - \left[\frac{3t^2 e^{-st}}{s^2} \right]_0^{\infty} + \int_0^{\infty} \frac{3 \times 2t \, e^{-st}}{s^2} \, dt$$

Integration by parts with $dv = e^{-st}$ and $u = t$ gives

$$F(s) = \left[\frac{t^3 e^{-st}}{-s} - \frac{3t^2 e^{-st}}{s^2} - \frac{3 \times 2t \, e^{-st}}{s^3} - \frac{3 \times 2 \, e^{-st}}{s^4} \right]_0^{\infty}$$

$$= \frac{3 \times 2}{s^4} = \frac{3!}{s^4} \qquad\qquad [7]$$

Review problems

1   Determine from first principles the Laplace transform of the function $f(t) = t$. Such a function is called a *unit ramp function* since it describes a function that increases at a constant rate. In this case the rate is 1.

2   Determine from first principles the Laplace transform of the function $f(t) = t^2$.

3   Determine from first principles the Laplace transform of the function $f(t) = 4t$. Such a function is a ramp function with a slope of 4.

4   Determine from first principles the Laplace transform of the function $f(t) = 4 + t$.

1.3 The unit step function

Figure 1.1 shows a graph of a unit step function. Such a function, when the step occurs at $t = 0$, has the equation

$f(t) = 1$ for all values of t greater than 0
$f(t) = 0$ for all values of t less than 0

The step function describes an abrupt change in some quantity from zero to a steady value, e.g. the change in the voltage applied to a circuit when it is suddenly switched on.

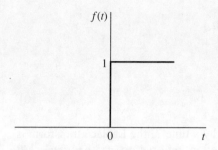

Fig. 1.1 A unit step function at $t = 0$

The unit step function thus cannot be described by $f(t) = 1$ since this would imply a function that has the constant value of 1 at all values of t, both positive and negative. The convention is usually adopted of describing the unit-step function that switches from 0 to $+1$ at $t = 0$ by the symbol $u(t)$ or $H(t)$, the H being after the man O.Heaviside. It is thus sometimes referred to as the *Heaviside function*.

The Laplace transform of this step function, for values greater than 0, is thus

$$\mathcal{L}\{u(t)\} = F(s) = \int_0^\infty 1e^{-st}\, dt$$

and so

$$F(s) = -\frac{1}{s}[e^{-st}]_0^\infty$$

Since, when $t = \infty$ the value of e^∞ is 0 and when $t = 0$ the value of e^{-0} is -1, then

$$F(s) = \frac{1}{s} \qquad\qquad [8]$$

Suppose now, instead of a unit step input signal of height 1 unit, we have one of height a units. Then, for all values of t greater than 0 we have $f(t) = a$ or, alternatively, we could write it as $au(t)$ or $aH(t)$, i.e. a multiplied by the unit step function. The Laplace transform of this function is

$$F(s) = \int_0^\infty a\, e^{-st}\, dt = a \int_0^\infty e^{-st}\, dt = \frac{a}{s} \qquad\qquad [9]$$

This is just a multiplied by the transform of the unit step.

Now consider a *delayed unit step function*, as illustrated in figure 1.2. We can think of this as representing a signal of magnitude 1 that is initially off and is then switched on and left on at the time $t = a$. The step occurs at a time T rather than 0. We thus have the function with value 1 when $t \geq T$ and 0 with $t < T$. This is just, when compared with figure 1.1, a shift of axes from 0 to a time T. Thus we replace the t in $u(t)$ by $t - T$ to give the function describing figure 1.2 as $u(t - T)$. The Laplace transform is then, for $T \geq 0$,

$$F(s) = \int_T^\infty e^{-st}u(t - T)\, dt$$

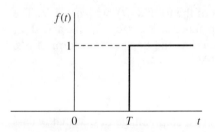

Fig. 1.2 The delayed unit step function

We can consider this integral as having two parts, from 0 to time T, when the function has the value 0, and from T to ∞, when it has the value 1. Thus we can write

$$F(s) = \int_0^T 0\,dt + \int_T^\infty 1e^{-st}\,dt$$

and so

$$F(s) = -\frac{1}{s}[e^{-st}]_T^\infty = \frac{e^{-sT}}{s} \qquad\qquad [10]$$

For any signal that is delayed by a time T, the Laplace transform is multiplied by e^{-sT}. This is often referred to as the *time shift theorem*.

Step functions can be used to define what might be termed a *window function*, i.e. the period of time in which some other function can occur. Thus $u(t) - u(t-4)$ is the addition of two functions $u(t)$ and $-u(t-4)$, as in figure 1.3, and thus defines a step that is one unit high and starts at $t = 0$ and continues until it is cancelled by a negative one unit step at $t = 4$. The function thus describes a rectangular pulse starting at $t = 0$ and having a duration of time of 4 units.

Example

Write the following function in terms of the Heaviside function: $f(t) = 0$ when we have $0 \le t < 4$ and $f(t) = 5$ when we have $t \ge 4$.

This is a step function of size 5 that occurs at a time $t = 4$. A step function of size 5 that occurs at $t = 0$ is written as $5u(t)$ and when it is delayed by 4 s it becomes $5u(t-4)$.

Example

What is the Laplace transform for a step voltage of size 4 V that starts at $t = 0$, i.e. a switch is closed and connects a steady voltage of 4 V into a circuit at the same time as a clock is started?

This voltage is a step function of the form $au(t)$, with $a = 4$ V. The Laplace transform of the step function of size 1 is $1/s$ and thus, since the step function of size a has the Laplace transform of a/s, the Laplace transform of the 4 V step is $4/s$.

Example

What is the Laplace transform of a step voltage of 4 V that occurs after a delay of 2 s, i.e. the switch connecting a constant 4 V into the circuit is closed 2 s after a clock has been started?

The step function is delayed by 2 s and can thus be represented by the function $u(t-2)$. For a delayed function the Laplace transform is that of the undelayed function, i.e. the function starting at $t = 0$, multiplied by e^{-sT}. Thus the Laplace transform is $(4/s)e^{-2s}$.

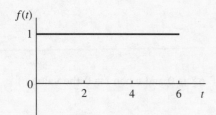

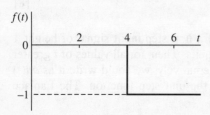

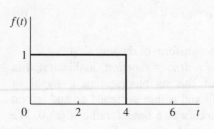

Fig. 1.3 $u(t) - u(t-4)$

Example

Represent the waveform shown in figure 1.4 by a function involving the Heaviside function.

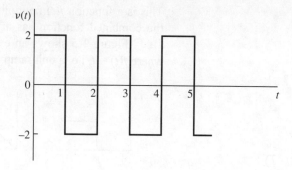

Fig. 1.4 Example

The step occurring at $t = 0$ can be represented by $2u(t)$. The step down at $t = 1$ can be represented by $-4u(t-1)$. The step up which occurs at $t = 2$ can be represented by $4u(t-2)$. The waveform can thus be represented by

$$2u(t) - 4u(t-1) + 4u(t-2) - 4u(t-3) + \ldots$$

Review problems

5   Write the following functions in terms of the Heaviside function:
(a) $f(t) = 5$ when $t \geq 0$,
(b) $f(t) = 0$ when $0 \leq t < 3$ and $f(t) = 2$ when $t \geq 3$,
(c) $f(t) = 0$ when $0 \leq t < 5$ and $f(t) = 3$ when $t \geq 5$.

6   Determine the Laplace transforms for the following:
(a) a 2 V step voltage occurs at $t = 0$,
(b) a 3 V step voltage occurs at $t = 2$,
(c) a 5 V step voltage occurs at $t = 4$.

7   Determine the Laplace transform of the function defined by $f(t) = 0$ when $0 \leq t < 6$ and $f(t) = 5$ when $t \geq 6$.

8   Determine the Laplace transform of the step function $u(t-4)$.

9   Determine, using the Heaviside function, the function and its Laplace transform which can be used to describe a single 0 to 4 V rectangular pulse with a leading edge at 20 ms and a pulse width of 15 ms.

1.3.1 Step function combined with other functions

The step function can be combined with other functions. Thus we can have a step multiplied by some function $f(t)$. For example if we have a delayed step then the combined function is

$$f(t)u(t-T)$$

This is a function $f(t)$ multiplied by 0 if $t < T$ and 1 if $t \geq T$. Thus the combined function has a value of 0 with $t < T$ and $f(t)$ with $t \geq T$. Figure 1.5 shows an example of such a combined function where $f(t) = t$, i.e. a unit ramp function.

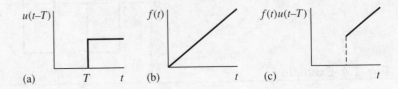

Fig. 1.5 $f(t)u(t-T)$

Example

Determine the function, and Laplace transform, which generates the waveform shown in figure 1.6.

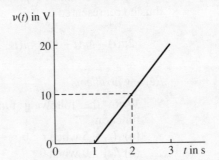

Fig. 1.6 Example

This waveform can be considered to be the product of a unit step waveform that has been delayed by 1 s, i.e. $u(t-1)$, and a ramp function of slope 10 V/s that has also been delayed by 1 s, i.e. $10(t-1)$. Thus the function describing the waveform can be written as $10(t-1)u(t-1)$.

The usefulness of including the step function is that it tells us that the combined function has a zero value for *all* values of time less than 1 s. This includes negative values of time. However, often the step function is omitted and it is assumed that $10(t-1)$ has a zero value when t is less than 1.

The waveform is just a ramp that has been delayed by 1 s and thus the Laplace transform is that of a ramp multiplied by e^{-Ts}, i.e.

$$F(s) = \frac{a}{s^2} e^{-Ts} = \frac{10\,e^{-1s}}{s^2}$$

Review problems

10 Determine the function that describes the waveform shown in figure 1.7.

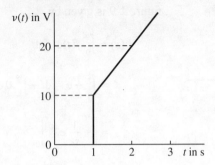

Fig. 1.7 Problem 10

11 Determine the function that describes the waveform shown in figure 1.8.

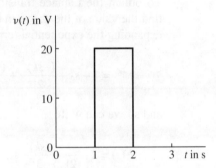

Fig. 1.8 Problem 11

12 Describe the function $(t-2)u(t-2)$ and determine its Laplace transform.

1.4 Impulse function

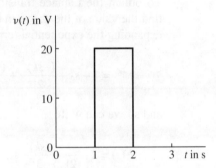

Fig. 1.9 Rectangular pulse

Consider a rectangular pulse of size $1/k$ that occurs at time $t = 0$ and which has a pulse width of k, i.e. the area of the pulse is 1. Figure 1.9 shows such a pulse. The pulse can be described as

$$f(t) = \frac{1}{k} \text{ for } 0 \le t < k$$
$$f(t) = 0 \text{ for } t > k$$

If we maintain this constant pulse area of 1 then if we decrease the width of the pulse, i.e. reduce k, so the height increases. In the limit as $k \to 0$ then we end up with just a vertical line at $t = 0$ with the height of the graph going off to infinity. The result is a graph that is zero except at a single point where there is an infinite spike (figure 1.10). Such a graph can be used to represent an impulse.

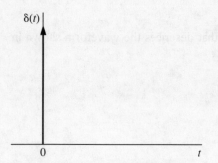

Fig. 1.10 The unit impulse function

The impulse is said to be a unit impulse because the area enclosed by it is 1. This function is represented by $\delta(t)$, being called the *unit impulse function* or the *Dirac-delta function*.

The Laplace transform for the unit area rectangular pulse in figure 1.9 is given by

$$F(s) = \int_0^\infty f(t)e^{-st}\,dt$$

$$= \int_0^k \frac{1}{k}e^{-st}\,dt + \int_k^\infty 0\,e^{-st}\,dt$$

$$= \left[-\frac{1}{sk}e^{-st}\right]_0^k$$

$$= -\frac{1}{sk}(e^{-sk} - 1)$$

To obtain the Laplace transform for the unit impulse we need to find the value of the above in the limit as $k \to 0$. We can do this by expanding the exponential term as a series. Thus

$$e^{-sk} = 1 - sk + \frac{(-sk)^2}{2!} + \frac{(-sk)^3}{3!} + \dots$$

and so we can write

$$F(s) = 1 - \frac{sk}{2!} + \frac{(sk)^2}{3!} + \dots$$

Thus in the limit as $k \to 0$ then the Laplace transform tends to the value 1.

$$\mathcal{L}\{\delta(t)\} = 1 \qquad\qquad [11]$$

Since the area of the above impulse is 1 we can define the size of such an impulse as being 1. Thus equation [11] gives the Laplace transform for a *unit impulse*.

An impulse of size a is represented by $a\delta(t)$. Hence the Laplace transform is

$$\mathcal{L}\{a\delta(t)\} = a \qquad\qquad [12]$$

A unit impulse which is delayed by a time T is written as $\delta(t - T)$ and has, using the time shift theorem, the Laplace transform of

$$\mathcal{L}\{\delta(t - T)\} = 1e^{-Ts} \qquad\qquad [13]$$

Example

Determine the Laplace transform of a 4 V impulse occurring in an electrical circuit at time $t = 0$.

The Laplace transform of a unit impulse occurring at $t = 0$ is 1. For an impulse of 4 V the transform will be 4.

Example

Determine the Laplace transform for a 4 V impulse occurring in an electrical circuit at time $t = 3$ s.

Delaying an impulse means the undelayed function is multiplied by e^{-Ts}. Thus the Laplace transform with $T = 3$ s is $4e^{-3s}$.

Example

What waveform is represented by the function $2\delta(t - 4)$ and what is its Laplace transform?

This describes an impulse of size 2 and occurring at a delayed time of $t = 4$. The Laplace transform of such a function is thus $2e^{-4s}$.

Review problems

13   What is the Laplace transform for an impulse of size 2 V that occurs at (a) $t = 0$, (b) $t = 5$ s?
14   What waveform is represented by the function $3\delta(t - 2)$ and what is its Laplace transform?
15   Write, in terms of the unit impulse function, the function describing an impulse of size 5 occurring at a delayed time of 3 s.
16   An electrical circuit has an input of pulses of constant size 2 V every 1/50 s, starting with the first one at $t = 0$. Write, in terms of the unit impulse function, the function describing the input.

1.5 Standard Laplace transforms

In determining the Laplace transforms of functions it is not usually necessary to go through the bother of evaluating integrals since tables are available that give the Laplace transforms of all the commonly occurring functions. These, when combined with a knowledge of the properties of such transforms (see section 1.6), enable most commonly encountered problems to be tackled. Table 1.1 lists some of the more common time functions and their Laplace transforms.

Table 1.1 Laplace transforms

Time function $f(t)$	*Laplace transform $F(s)$*
1 $\delta(t)$, unit impulse	1
2 $\delta(t - T)$, delayed unit impulse	e^{-sT}
3 $u(t)$, a unit step	$\dfrac{1}{s}$
4 $u(t - T)$, a delayed unit step	$\dfrac{e^{-sT}}{s}$
5 t, a unit ramp	$\dfrac{1}{s^2}$
6 t^n, nth order ramp	$\dfrac{n!}{s^{n+1}}$
7 e^{-at}, exponential decay	$\dfrac{1}{s+a}$
8 $1 - e^{-at}$, exponential growth	$\dfrac{a}{s(s+a)}$
9 $t e^{-at}$	$\dfrac{1}{(s+a)^2}$
10 $t^n e^{-at}$	$\dfrac{n!}{(s+a)^{n+1}}$
11 $t - \dfrac{1 - e^{-at}}{a}$	$\dfrac{a}{s^2(s+a)}$
12 $e^{-at} - e^{-bt}$	$\dfrac{b-a}{(s+a)(s+b)}$
13 $(1 - at)e^{-at}$	$\dfrac{s}{(s+a)^2}$
14 $1 - \dfrac{b}{b-a}e^{-at} + \dfrac{a}{b-a}e^{-bt}$	$\dfrac{ab}{s(s+a)(s+b)}$
15 $\dfrac{e^{-at}}{(b-a)(c-a)} + \dfrac{e^{-bt}}{(c-a)(a-b)} + \dfrac{e^{-ct}}{(a-c)(b-c)}$	$\dfrac{1}{(s+a)(s+b)(s+c)}$
16 $\sin \omega t$, a sine wave	$\dfrac{\omega}{s^2 + \omega^2}$
17 $\cos \omega t$, a cosine wave	$\dfrac{s}{s^2 + \omega^2}$
18 $e^{-at}\sin \omega t$, a damped sine wave	$\dfrac{\omega}{(s+a)^2 + \omega^2}$
19 $e^{-at}\cos \omega t$, a damped cosine wave	$\dfrac{s+a}{(s+a)^2 + \omega^2}$
20 $1 - \cos \omega t$	$\dfrac{\omega^2}{s(s^2 + \omega^2)}$
21 $t \cos \omega t$	$\dfrac{s^2 - \omega^2}{(s^2 + \omega^2)^2}$
22 $t \sin \omega t$	$\dfrac{2\omega s}{(s^2 + \omega^2)^2}$

Time function $f(t)$	Laplace transform $F(s)$
23 $\sin(\omega t + \theta)$	$\dfrac{\omega\cos\theta + s\sin\theta}{s^2+\omega^2}$
24 $\cos(\omega t + \theta)$	$\dfrac{s\cos\theta - \omega\sin\theta}{s^2+\omega^2}$
25 $e^{-at}\sin(\omega t + \theta)$	$\dfrac{(s+a)\sin\theta + \omega\cos\theta}{(s+a)^2+\omega^2}$
26 $e^{-at}\cos(\omega t + \theta)$	$\dfrac{(s+a)\cos\theta - \omega\sin\theta}{(s+a)^2+\omega^2}$
27 $\dfrac{\omega}{\sqrt{1-\zeta^2}}e^{-\zeta\omega t}\sin\omega\sqrt{1-\zeta^2}\,t$	$\dfrac{\omega^2}{s^2+2\zeta\omega s+\omega^2}$
28 $1 - \dfrac{1}{\sqrt{1-\zeta^2}}e^{-\zeta\omega t}\sin\left(\omega\sqrt{1-\zeta^2}\,t+\phi\right)$, $\cos\phi = \zeta$	$\dfrac{\omega^2}{s(s^2+2\zeta\omega s+\omega^2)}$
29 $\sinh\omega t$	$\dfrac{\omega}{s^2-\omega^2}$
30 $\cosh\omega t$	$\dfrac{s}{s^2-\omega^2}$
31 $e^{-at}\sinh\omega t$	$\dfrac{\omega}{(s+a)^2-\omega^2}$
32 $e^{-at}\cosh\omega t$	$\dfrac{s+a}{(s+a)^2-\omega^2}$
33 Half-wave rectified sine, period $T = 2\pi/\omega$	$\dfrac{\omega}{(s^2+\omega^2)(1-e^{-\pi s/\omega})}$
34 Full-wave rectified sine, period $T = 2\pi/\omega$	$\dfrac{\omega}{(s^2+\omega^2)}\dfrac{(1+e^{-\pi s/\omega})}{(1-e^{-\pi s/\omega})}$
35 Rectangular pulses, period T, amplitude $+1$ to 0	$\dfrac{1}{s(1+e^{-sT/2})}$

Note: $f(t) = 0$ for all negative values of t. The $u(t)$ terms have been omitted from most of the time functions and have to be assumed.

Example

Determine, using table 1.1, the Laplace transforms for the time functions (a) t^4, (b) $\sin\omega t$, (c) te^{-at}.

(a) Using item 6 in the table, the Laplace transform is

$$F(s) = \frac{4!}{s^{4+1}} = \frac{24}{s^5}$$

(b) Using item 16 in the table, the Laplace transform is

$$F(s) = \frac{\omega}{s^2 + \omega^2}$$

(c) Using item 9 in the table, the Laplace transform is

$$F(s) = \frac{1}{(s+a)^2}$$

Review problems

17 Determine, using table 1.1, the Laplace transforms for the time functions (a) $\cos \omega t$, (b) $1 - e^{-at}$, (c) t^5, (d) $1 - \cos \omega t$.

1.6 Properties of Laplace transforms

In this section the basic properties of the Laplace transform are considered. These properties enable the table of standard Laplace transforms to be used in a wide range of situations.

1.6.1 Linearity property

If two separate time functions, e.g. $f(t)$ and $g(t)$, have Laplace transforms then the transform of the sum of the time functions is the sum of the two separate Laplace transforms.

$$\mathcal{L}\{af(t) + bg(t)\} = a\mathcal{L}f(t) + b\mathcal{L}g(t) \qquad [14]$$

a and b are constants.

This can be shown to be true by considering, from first principles, the transform of the sum of the two time functions. Thus

$$\mathcal{L}\{af(t) + bg(t)\} = \int_0^\infty [af(t) + bg(t)]e^{-st}\,dt$$

$$= a\int_0^\infty f(t)e^{-st}\,dt + b\int_0^\infty g(t)e^{-st}\,dt$$

$$= \mathcal{L}af(t) + \mathcal{L}bg(t)$$

Example

What is the Laplace transform of $1 + 2t + 4t^2$?

Using the linearity property then the Laplace transform will be the sum of the transforms of the individual terms in the expression. Thus, using items 1, 5 and 6 in table 1.1,

$$F(s) = \frac{1}{s} + \frac{2}{s^2} + \frac{8}{s^3}$$

Example

What is the Laplace transform of $2\,e^{-3t} + 5\,e^{-2t}$?

Using the linearity property then the Laplace transform will be the sum of the transforms of the individual terms in the expression. Thus, using item 7 in table 1.1,

$$F(s) = \frac{2}{s+3} + \frac{5}{s+2}$$

Example

Determine the Laplace transform of the signal giving the graph shown in figure 1.11.

This signal can be considered to be the sum of a step function of size 10 V plus a ramp function $5t$, both starting at $t = 0$. Thus the Laplace transform is

$$F(s) = \frac{10}{s} + \frac{5}{s^2}$$

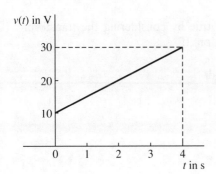

Fig. 1.11 Example

Example

Use the trigonometric identity

$$\sin(A + B) = \sin A \cos B + \cos A \sin B$$

to determine the Laplace transform of $\sin(\omega t + \theta)$.

We thus have

$$\sin(\omega t + \theta) = \sin \omega t \cos \theta + \cos \omega t \sin \theta$$

Hence using the Laplace transforms given in table 1.1, items 16 and 17, then

$$\mathcal{L}\{\sin(\omega t + \theta)\} = \frac{\omega \cos \theta}{s^2 + \omega^2} + \frac{s \sin \theta}{s^2 + \omega^2}$$

Review problems

18 Determine the Laplace transforms of the following:
(a) $2 \sin 4t - 5 \cos 2t$, (b) $3 + 2t - 5t^2 + 3t^3$, (c) $5 \cos 4t - 6$.

19 Determine the Laplace transform of a signal that can be considered to be the sum of a step function of size 2 V and a ramp function of $3t$.

20 Determine the Laplace transform of a signal that can be considered to be the sum of a step function of size 4 and an exponential growth function e^{2t}.

1.6.2 *s*-domain shifting property

This property is used to determine the Laplace transform of functions that have an exponential factor and is sometimes referred to as the *first shifting property*. If $F(s) = \mathcal{L}\{f(t)\}$ then

$$\mathcal{L}\{e^{at}f(t)\} = F(s - a) \qquad\qquad [15]$$

This can be shown to be true by considering the transform from first principles of the function. If

$$\mathcal{L}\{f(t)\} = F(s) = \int_0^\infty f(t)e^{-st}\, dt$$

then

$$\mathcal{L}\{e^{at}f(t)\} = \int_0^\infty e^{at}f(t)e^{-st}\, dt$$

$$= \int_0^\infty e^{-(s-a)t}f(t)\, dt$$

$$= F(s - a)$$

Hence the substitution of $s - a$ for s corresponds to multiplication of the function by e^{at}.

Example

Determine the Laplace transform of $e^{at}t^n$.

The Laplace transform of t^n is given by item 6 in table 1.1 as

$$\mathcal{L}\{t^n\} = \frac{n!}{s^{n+1}}$$

Thus, using equation [14],

$$\mathcal{L}\{e^{at}t^n\} = \frac{n!}{(s - a)^{n+1}}$$

Example

Determine the Laplace transform of $e^{-2t}\cos 3t$.

The Laplace transform of $\cos 3t$ is given by item 17 in table 1.1 as

$$\mathcal{L}\{\cos 3t\} = \frac{s}{s^2 + \omega^2}$$

Thus, using equation [14],

$$\mathcal{L}\{e^{-2t}\cos 3t\} = \frac{s+2}{(s+2)^2 + \omega^2}$$

Example

Determine the Laplace transform of $2\,e^{3t}\sin^2 t$.

Since $\cos 2t = 1 - 2\sin^2 t$, then

$$\mathcal{L}\{2\sin^2 t\} = \mathcal{L}\{2 \times \tfrac{1}{2}(1 - \cos 2t)\}$$

$$= \frac{1}{s} - \frac{s}{s^2 + 4}$$

Thus, using equation [14],

$$\mathcal{L}\{2\,e^{3t}\sin^2 t\} = \frac{1}{(s-3)} - \frac{s-3}{(s-3)^2 + 4}$$

Review problems

21   Determine the Laplace transforms of the following:
(a) $2\,e^{2t}t^3$, (b) $3\,e^{-3t}\sin 4t$, (c) $2\,e^{4t}\cos 2t$, (d) $6\,e^t\sin^2 t$,
(e) $4\,e^t\cos^2 t$.

1.6.3 Time domain shifting property

If a signal is delayed by a time T then its Laplace transform is multiplied by e^{-sT}. If $F(s)$ is the Laplace transform of $f(t)$ then

$$\mathcal{L}\{f(t-T)u(t-T)\} = e^{-sT}F(s) \tag{16}$$

This delaying of a signal by a time T is referred to as the *second shift theorem*. See section 1.3 for a derivation of the theorem.

The time domain shifting property can be applied to all Laplace transforms. Thus for an impulse $\delta(t)$ which is delayed by a time T to give the function $\delta(t-T)$, then the Laplace transform of

$\delta(t)$, namely 1, is multiplied by e^{-sT} to give $1e^{-sT}$ as the transform for the delayed function.

Example

What is the Laplace transform of the function $e^{2(t-3)}u(t-3)$?

This is the exponential function e^{2t} that has a start that is delayed by a time of 3. The Laplace transform is thus that of e^{2t} multiplied by e^{-3s}, i.e.

$$\mathcal{L}\{e^{2(t-3)}u(t-3)\} = \frac{e^{-3s}}{s-2}$$

Example

What is the Laplace transform of the function defined by $f(t) = 0$ if $0 \le t < 5$ and $f(t) = (t-5)^2$ if $t \ge 5$?

This is just the function $f(t) = t^2$ delayed by a time of 5. Thus the Laplace transform is

$$\frac{2e^{-5t}}{s^3}$$

Example

What is the Laplace transform of a single pulse that consists of just the first half-cycle of a sine wave, as illustrated in figure 1.12.

We can obtain this function by considering it to be the sum of a sine function, extending over many cycles, and a sine function that has been delayed by half a cycle, i.e. $\frac{1}{2}T$ with T being the time taken for one complete cycle. The function is thus

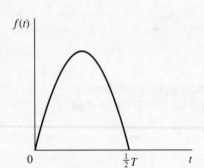

$f(t)$

0 $\frac{1}{2}T$ t

Fig. 1.12 Example

$$f(t) = \sin\omega t\, u(t) + \sin\omega\left(t - \tfrac{1}{2}T\right)u\left(t - \tfrac{1}{2}T\right)$$

where $\omega = 2\pi/T$. Thus

$$F(s) = \frac{\omega}{s^2 + \omega^2} + \frac{\omega\, e^{-sT/2}}{s^2 + \omega^2} \qquad [17]$$

Review problems

22 What is the Laplace transform of the function giving $f(t) = 0$ if $0 \le t < 2$ and $f(t) = (t-2)^2$ if $t \ge 2$?
23 What is the Laplace transform of the function represented by $2(t-10)u(t-10)$?

24 What is the Laplace transform of the exponential function e^{-3t} if instead of starting at $t = 0$ it starts at $t = 5$?

1.6.4 Periodic functions

For a function $f(t)$ which is a periodic function of period T then the Laplace transform of that function is

$$\mathcal{L}f(t) = \frac{1}{1 - e^{-sT}} F_1(s) \qquad [18]$$

where $F_1(s)$ is the Laplace transform of the function for the first period.

This can be proved by considering the periodic function to be the sum of the function $f_1(t)$ describing the first period, the first period function when it is delayed by 1 period, the first period function when it is delayed by 2 periods, the first period function when it is delayed by 3 periods, etc.

$$f(t) = f_1(t)u(t) + f_1(t - T)u(t - T) + f_1(t - 2T)u(t - 2T) + \ldots$$

The Laplace transform of the periodic function is thus

$$\mathcal{L}\{f(t)\} = F_1(s) + e^{-sT}F_1(s) + e^{-2sT}F_1(s) + \ldots$$

$$= (1 + e^{-sT} + e^{-2sT} + \ldots)F_1(s)$$

The term in the brackets is a geometric series and has the sum to infinity of $1/(1 - e^{-sT})$. Thus

$$\mathcal{L}\{f(t)\} = \frac{1}{1 - e^{-sT}} F_1(s)$$

Example

Determine the Laplace transform of a full-wave rectified sine wave that starts at $t = 0$, figure 1.13 showing the form of such a signal.

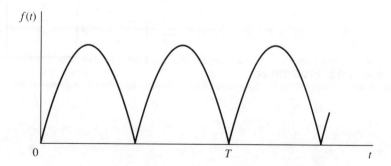

Fig. 1.13 Example

The Laplace transform for the first half-cycle of the wave is given by equation [17] as

$$F_1(s) = \frac{\omega}{s^2 + \omega^2} + \frac{\omega\, e^{-sT/2}}{s^2 + \omega^2}$$

$$= \frac{\omega}{s^2 + \omega^2}(1 + e^{-sT/2})$$

Therefore the periodic wave has the transform

$$F(s) = \frac{1}{1 - e^{-sT/2}} F_1(s)$$

$$= \frac{\omega}{s^2 + \omega^2} \frac{1 + e^{-sT/2}}{1 - e^{-sT/2}}$$

Review problems

25 Determine the Laplace transform for the periodic waveform shown in figure 1.14.

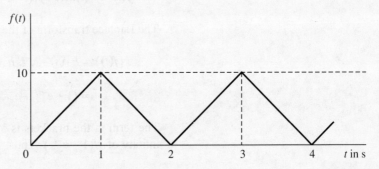

Fig. 1.14 Problem 25

26 Determine the Laplace transform for the periodic waveform shown in figure 1.15.

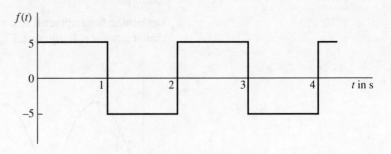

Fig. 1.15 Problem 26

Further problems

27 Determine from first principles the Laplace transform of
   (a) sin at, (b) cos at.

28 Write, using the unit step notation, the functions that describe
   the following:
   (a) a step voltage of size 10 V starting at $t = 0$,
   (b) a step voltage of size 10 V starting at $t = 2$ s,
   (c) a single 0 to 4 V rectangular pulse with a leading edge at
   0.2 s and with a pulse width of 0.1 s,
   (d) a single sawtooth pulse that starts at 1 s and rises at the
   rate of 4 V/s for 2 s before dropping abruptly to zero.

29 Use the impulse function to write functions describing the
   following:
   (a) an impulse of size 6 V occurring at $t = 0$,
   (b) an impulse of size 6 V occurring at $t = 4$ s,
   (c) impulses of size 6 V occurring every 1 s.

30 Using table 1.1, determine the Laplace transforms for:
   (a) a step voltage of size 5 V which starts at $t = 0$ s,
   (b) a step voltage of size 5 V which starts at $t = 3$ s,
   (c) a ramp voltage of 5 V/s which starts at $t = 0$ s,
   (d) a ramp voltage of 5 V/s which starts at $t = 3$ s,
   (e) an impulse of size 5 V at $t = 0$ s,
   (f) an impulse of size 5 V at $t = 3$ s,
   (g) a sinusoidal signal of amplitude 5 V and frequency 50 Hz
   that starts at $t = 0$ s,
   (h) a sinusoidal signal of amplitude 5 V and frequency 50 Hz
   that starts at $t = 3$ s.

31 Determine, using table 1.1, the Laplace transforms for:
   (a) e^{-2t}, (b) $4 e^{-2t}$, (c) $4(1 - e^{-2t})$, (d) $5 + 4(1 - e^{-2t})$,
   (e) $1 + 2t - 3t^2$, (f) $2 e^{2t} - 3 e^{-3t}$, (g) $4 \sin 2t - 3 \cos 2t$,
   (h) $e^{-2t} \sin 3t$, (i) $1 - \cos 4t$.

32 Determine the Laplace transforms of the following voltages
   that vary with time according to:
   (a) $v = 5(1 - e^{-t/50})$ volts, (b) $10 + 5(1 - e^{-t/50})$ volts,
   (c) $5e^{-t/50}$ volts.

33 Determine the Laplace transforms for a unit rectangular pulse
   of duration 3 s that starts (a) at $t = 0$, (b) at $t = 2$ s.

34 Determine the Laplace transforms for the following:
   (a) $f(t) = 0$ for $0 \le t < 2$ and $f(t) = t - 2$ for $2 \le t$,
   (b) $f(t) = 0$ for $0 \le t < 3$ and $f(t) = e^{t-3}$ for $3 \le t$,
   (c) $f(t) = 0$ for $0 \le t < 4$ and $f(t) = 2(t - 4)$ for $4 \le t$.

35 Determine, using

$$\cos(A + B) = \cos A \cos B - \sin A \sin B$$

   the Laplace transform for $\cos(\omega t + \theta)$ and hence that for
   $e^{-at} \cos(\omega t + \theta)$.

36 Determine the Laplace transform for the periodic function of a
   square wave that has its first cycle represented by $f(t) = 3$ for

$0 \leq t < 2$ and $f(t) = -3$ for $2 \leq t < 4$, and has a periodic time of 4.

37 Determine the Laplace transform for the periodic function of a sawtooth wave that has its first cycle represented by $f(t) = t$ for $0 \leq t < 1$ and has a periodic time of 1.

38 Represent the hyperbolic functions sinh at and cosh at in terms of the exponential functions, i.e.

$$\sinh at = \frac{e^{at} - e^{-at}}{2}$$

$$\cosh at = \frac{e^{at} + e^{-at}}{2}$$

and hence determine their Laplace transforms.

39 By representing the hyperbolic functions sinh and cosh in terms of exponential functions, as in the previous problem, determine the Laplace transforms of:
(a) $\cosh at \cos at$, (b) $\cosh at \sin at$, (c) $\sinh at \cos at$, (d) $\sinh at \sin at$.

2 Inverse Laplace transform

2.1 The inverse transformation

As mentioned in chapter 1, the Laplace transform can be used to solve differential equations. The procedure used is to transform from the time domain to the s-domain, carry out algebraic manipulations of the equation and then transform back to the time domain. This transformation back to the time domain is known as the inverse Laplace transformation.

The inverse Laplace transformation is the conversion of a Laplace transform $F(s)$ into a function of time $f(t)$. This operation can be written as

$$\mathcal{L}^{-1}\{F(s)\} = f(t) \qquad [1]$$

The inverse operation can generally be carried out by using table 1.1, since the functions of s appear in a standard form given in the table, or at least one that can be readily converted into such a form.

The linearity property of Laplace transforms (see section 1.6.1 and equation [14]) means that if we have a transform as the sum of two separate terms then we can take the inverse of each separately and the sum of the two inverse transforms is the required inverse transform.

$$\mathcal{L}^{-1}\{aF(s) + bG(s)\} = a\mathcal{L}^{-1}F(s) + b\mathcal{L}^{-1}G(s) \qquad [2]$$

Example

Determine, using table 1.1, the inverse transformations of

(a) $\dfrac{5}{s}$, (b) $\dfrac{3}{2s+1}$, (c) $\dfrac{2}{s-6}$

To use table 1.1 to obtain the inverse transformations means looking through the table to find the Laplace transform which is of the same basic form.

(a) The table includes a Laplace transform, item 3, of $1/s$ and thus since this is just the item we are concerned with multiplied by the constant 5 the inverse transformation will be the function that gives $1/s$, i.e. 1, multiplied by the same constant. The inverse transformation is thus 5.

(b) This transform can be rearranged to give

$$\frac{3(1/2)}{s + (1/2)}$$

The table contains the transform $1/(s + a)$, item 7 with the inverse of e^{-at}. Thus the inverse transformation is just this multiplied by the constant $(3/2)$ with $a = (1/2)$, i.e. $(3/2)e^{-t/2}$.

(c) This transform is of the form $1/(s + a)$, item 7, with $a = -6$. Thus the inverse transformation is $2\,e^{6t}$

Example

Determine the inverse Laplace transform of

(a) $\dfrac{5s}{s^2 + 9}$, (b) $\dfrac{4}{s^2 - 6s + 13}$

(a) Table 1.1, item 17, contains the transform

$$\mathcal{L}^{-1}\left\{\frac{s}{s^2 + \omega^2}\right\} = \cos \omega t$$

The expression in (a) can be converted to this form.

$$5\frac{s}{s^2 + 3^2}$$

Thus the inverse transform is $5 \cos 3t$.

(b) Table 1.1, item 18, contains the transform

$$\mathcal{L}^{-1}\left\{\frac{\omega}{(s+a)^2 + \omega^2}\right\} = e^{-at}\sin \omega t$$

The expression in (b) can be converted into the form

$$2\frac{2}{(s-3)^2 + 2^2}$$

and thus the inverse transform is $2\,e^{3t}\sin 2t$.

Example

Determine the inverse Laplace transform of $(2s+2)/(s^2+1)$.

This expression can be rearranged as

$$2\left[\frac{s}{s^2+1}+\frac{1}{s^2+1}\right]$$

The first term in the brackets has the inverse transform of $\cos t$, item 17 in table 1.1, and the second term $\sin t$, item 16 in table 1.1. Thus the inverse transform of the expression is

$$2\cos t+2\sin t$$

Review problems

1   Determine the inverse Laplace transformations of

(a) $\dfrac{5}{s+10}$, (b) $\dfrac{4}{s^2}$, (c) $\dfrac{2}{s(s+2)}$, (d) $\dfrac{12}{s^4}$, (e) $\dfrac{3}{s-2}$,

(f) $\dfrac{2s}{s^2-16}$, (g) $\dfrac{4}{s^2+1}$, (h) $\dfrac{2}{s^2+4}$, (i) $\dfrac{4s}{s^2+9}$,

(j) $\dfrac{2s+4}{s^2+4s+20}$, (k) $\dfrac{3}{s^2+4s+7}$, (l) $\dfrac{18}{s^2-2s-8}$,

(m) $\dfrac{s+1}{s^2+2s+5}$, (n) $\dfrac{s+3}{s^2+6s+13}$

2   Determine the inverse Laplace transformations of

(a) $\dfrac{2s+4}{s^3}$, (b) $\dfrac{s-9}{s^2+9}$, (c) $\dfrac{s-12}{s+4}$, (d) $\dfrac{4s^2+2}{s^4}$

2.2 Partial fractions

Often $F(s)$ is a ratio of two polynomials, i.e. of the form

$$\frac{a_n s^n + a_{n-1}s^{n-1} + \ldots + a_1 s + a_0}{b_m s^m + b_{m-1}s^{m-1} + \ldots + b_1 s + b_0}$$

and cannot be readily identified with a standard transform in table 1.1. It has to be converted into simple fraction terms before the standard transforms can be used. The process of converting an expression into simple fraction terms is called decomposing into *partial fractions*. This technique can be used provided the degree of the numerator is less than the degree of the denominator, i.e. in the above equation n is less than m. The degree of a polynomial is the highest power of s in the expression.

When the degree of the numerator is equal to or higher than that of the denominator, the denominator must be divided into the numerator until the result is the sum of terms with the remainder fractional term having a numerator of lower degree than the denominator.

In general, the denominator of the ratio of two polynomials can be written as a product of a number of factors, of the form $(s-a)$ or $(s^2 + as + b)$. For example,

$$\frac{3s+4}{s^2+3s+2}$$

has a numerator with a degree 1 and a denominator with a degree 2. The denominator is a product of the factors $(s + 1)$ and $(s + 2)$. We can then decompose the expression into the partial fractions

$$\frac{3s+4}{(s+1)(s+2)} = \frac{1}{s+1} + \frac{2}{s+2}$$

We can consider there to be basically three types of partial fractions:

1   The denominator contains factors which are only of the form $(s + a)$, $(s + b)$, $(s + c)$, etc. The expression is of the form

$$\frac{f(s)}{(s+a)(s+b)(s+c)}$$

and has the partial fractions of

$$\frac{A}{(s+a)} + \frac{B}{(s+b)} + \frac{C}{(s+c)}$$

2   There are repeated $(s + a)$ factors in the denominator, i.e. the denominator contains powers of such a factor and the expression is of the form

$$\frac{f(s)}{(s+a)^n}$$

This then has partial fractions of

$$\frac{A}{(s+a)^1} + \frac{B}{(s+a)^2} + \frac{C}{(s+a)^3} + \dots \frac{N}{(s+a)^n}$$

3   The denominator contains quadratic factors and the quadratic does not factorise without imaginary terms. For an expression of the form

$$\frac{f(s)}{(as^2 + bs + c)(s + d)}$$

the partial fractions are

$$\frac{As + B}{as^2 + bs + c} + \frac{C}{(s + d)}$$

The values of the constants A, B, C, etc. can be found by either making use of the fact that the equality between the expression and the partial fractions must be true for all values of s or that the coefficients of s^n in the expression must equal those of s^n in the partial fraction expansion. The use of the first method is illustrated by the following example where the partial fractions of

$$\frac{3s + 4}{(s + 1)(s + 2)} \quad \text{are} \quad \frac{A}{s + 1} + \frac{B}{s + 2}$$

Then, for the expressions to be equal, we must have

$$\frac{3s + 4}{(s + 1)(s + 2)} = \frac{A(s + 2) + B(s + 1)}{(s + 1)(s + 2)}$$

and consequently

$$3s + 4 = A(s + 2) + B(s + 1)$$

This must be true for all values of s. The procedure is then to pick values of s that will enable some of the terms involving constants to become zero and so enable other constants to be determined. Thus if we let $s = -2$ then we have

$$3(-2) + 4 = A(-2 + 2) + B(-2 + 1)$$

and so $B = 2$. If we now let $s = -1$ then

$$3(-1) + 4 = A(-1 + 2) + B(-1 + 1)$$

and so $A = 1$. Thus

$$\frac{3s + 4}{(s + 1)(s + 2)} = \frac{1}{s + 1} + \frac{2}{s + 2}$$

Example

Determine the partial fractions of

(a) $\dfrac{s-6}{(s-1)(s-2)}$, (b) $\dfrac{s+5}{s^2+3s+2}$, (c) $\dfrac{2s-19}{(s-2)^2(s+3)}$,

(d) $\dfrac{3s}{(s^2-2s+5)(s+1)}$

(a) The partial fractions for this expression can be written as

$$\frac{s-6}{(s-1)(s-2)} = \frac{A}{s-1} + \frac{B}{s-2}$$

$$= \frac{A(s-2)+B(s-1)}{(s-1)(s-2)}$$

Thus

$$s-6 = A(s-2)+B(s-1)$$

This must be true for all values of s. Hence if we consider $s = 2$ then $B = -4$. If we consider $s = 1$ then $A = 5$. Thus the partial fractions are

$$\frac{5}{s-1} - \frac{4}{s-2}$$

(b) This expression can be written as

$$\frac{s+5}{s^2+3s+2} = \frac{s+5}{(s+1)(s+2)} = \frac{A}{s+1} + \frac{B}{s+2}$$

Thus we must have

$$A(s+2)+B(s+1) = s+5$$

Hence, if we choose $s = -2$ then $B = -3$. With $s = -1$ then $A = 4$. Thus the partial fractions are

$$\frac{4}{s+1} - \frac{3}{s+2}$$

(c) This expression involves a repeated factor and is thus written in partial factor form as

$$\frac{2s-19}{(s-2)^2(s+3)} = \frac{A}{(s-2)^2} + \frac{B}{(s-2)} + \frac{C}{(s+3)}$$

Thus we must have

$$A(s+3)+B(s-2)(s+3)+C(s-2)^2 = 2s-19$$

Hence with $s=-3$ then $25C=-6-19$ and so $C=-1$. With $s=2$ then $5A = 4-19$ and so $A=-3$. With $s=0$ then

$$3A - 6B + 4C = -19$$

Using the values of A and C already obtained, then $B=1$. Thus the partial fractions are

$$-\frac{3}{(s-2)^2} + \frac{1}{(s-2)} - \frac{1}{(s+3)}$$

(d) This expression involves a quadratic and thus

$$\frac{3s}{(s^2 - 2s + 5)(s+1)} = \frac{A+Bs}{(s^2-2s+5)} + \frac{C}{(s+3)}$$

Hence

$$(A+Bs)(s+3)+C(s^2-2s+5) = 3s$$

With $s=-3$ then $C=-\frac{9}{20}$. With $s=0$ then $3A+5C=0$ and so $A=\frac{3}{4}$. With $s=1$ then

$$4(A+B)+4C = 3$$

and hence $B = \frac{9}{20}$. Thus the partial fractions are

$$\frac{15+9s}{20(s^2-2s+5)} - \frac{9}{20(s+3)}$$

Example

Determine the partial fractions of

$$\frac{2s^2 + 2}{(s+4)(s-2)}$$

This expression has a numerator of the same degree as the denominator. Thus division has to be used to put the expression into a form with a numerator having a lower degree than the denominator.

$$\begin{array}{r} 2 \hspace{3cm} \\ s^2 + 2s - 8\overline{\smash{\big)}\,2s^2 + 2} \\ 2s^2 + 4s - 16 \\ \hline -4s + 18 \end{array}$$

The expression can now be written as

$$2 + \frac{-4s + 18}{(s+4)(s-2)}$$

Normal partial fraction procedure can now be used for the fraction.

$$\frac{-4s + 18}{(s+4)(s-2)} = \frac{A}{s+4} + \frac{B}{s-2}$$

$$-4s + 18 = A(s-2) + B(s+4)$$

With $s = 2$ then $B = \frac{5}{3}$. With $s = -4$ then $A = -\frac{17}{3}$. Thus the expression can be written as

$$2 - \frac{17}{3(s+4)} + \frac{5}{3(s-2)}$$

Review problems

3 Determine the partial fractions of

(a) $\dfrac{s-8}{(s+1)(s-2)}$, (b) $\dfrac{s+1}{s(s-2)(s+3)}$, (c) $\dfrac{3s+2}{s^2+6s+8}$,

(d) $\dfrac{3s}{(s^2+1)(s-1)}$, (e) $\dfrac{4}{(s-1)^2(s+1)}$, (f) $\dfrac{5s^2+10}{(s+4)(s-2)}$

4 Determine the inverse transforms of

(a) $\dfrac{1}{(s+a)(s+b)}$, (b) $\dfrac{4(s+1)}{s^2+16}$, (c) $\dfrac{3s+1}{s^2+4s}$,

(d) $\dfrac{2(3s+1)}{(s-1)(s+3)}$, (e) $\dfrac{2s+12}{(s^2+5s+6)(s+1)}$, (f) $\dfrac{2(2s-7)}{(s-3)(s-1)}$,

(g) $\dfrac{2[s^2+9(s-1)]}{s(s^2-9)}$

2.3 Using Laplace transform properties

The properties of Laplace transforms described in section 1.6 can be used to determine rules for dealing with some inverse Laplace transforms. The following are some generally useful ones.

2.3.1 $(s - a)$ factor

The s-domain shifting property, section 1.6.2 and equation [15], can be written in inverse form as

$$\mathcal{L}^{-1}\{F(s-a)\} = e^{at}f(t) \tag{3}$$

Thus if the inverse transform contains a term of the form $(s-a)$, then replace it by s and determine the inverse Laplace transform of the resulting expression. When multiplied by e^{at} this gives the required inverse transform.

Example

Determine the inverse Laplace transform of $1/(s+3)^4$.

If we use equation [1] and take $a = -3$, then we are now involved in determining the inverse transform of $1/s^4$. Since this is $t^3/6$ (item 6, table 1.1), then the required inverse transform is $\frac{1}{6}t^3e^{-3t}$.

Example

Determine the inverse Laplace transform of

$$\frac{3s+10}{s^2+4s+20}$$

This expression can be written as

$$\frac{3(s+2)+4}{(s+2)^2+16} = \frac{3(s+2)}{(s+2)^2+4^2} + \frac{4}{(s+2)^2+4^2}$$

The first term can be considered to be an expression for which there has been an s shift of 2. Thus, with the inverse transform

$$\mathcal{L}^{-1}\left\{\frac{3s}{s^2+4^2}\right\} = 3\cos 4t$$

then

$$\mathcal{L}^{-1}\left\{\frac{3(s+2)}{(s+2)^2+4^2}\right\} = 3\,e^{-2t}\cos 4t$$

The second term can also be considered to be an expression for which there has been an s shift of 2. With the inverse transform

$$\mathcal{L}^{-1}\left\{\frac{4}{s^2+4^2}\right\} = 4\sin 4t$$

then

$$\mathcal{L}^{-1}\left\{\frac{4}{(s+2)^2+4^2}\right\} = 4\,e^{-2t}\sin 4t$$

Thus the inverse transform is

$$3\,e^{-2t}\cos 4t + 4\,e^{-2t}\sin 4t$$

Review problems

5   Determine the inverse Laplace transform of

(a) $\dfrac{2}{(s+2)^3}$, (b) $\dfrac{6}{(s-2)^3}$,

(c) $\dfrac{8}{s^2+4s+20}$, (d) $\dfrac{s+2}{s^2-4s-4}$

2.3.2 e⁻ˢᵀ factor

The time domain shifting property, section 1.6.3 and equation [16], can be written in inverse form as

$$\mathcal{L}^{-1}\{e^{-sT}F(s)\} = f(t-T)u(t-T) \qquad [4]$$

Thus if the inverse transform numerator contains an e^{-sT} factor then remove the e^{-sT} from it and determine the inverse Laplace transform of what remains. The exponential factor can then be taken into account by substituting $(t-T)$ for t in the result.

Example

Determine the inverse Laplace transform of

$$\frac{5e^{-3s}}{(s+2)^2}$$

Removing the e^{-3s} term from the expression leaves

$$\mathcal{L}^{-1}\left\{\frac{5}{(s+2)^2}\right\} = 5t\,e^{-2t}u(t)$$

Thus the inverse Laplace transform of the original expression is

$$5(t-3)e^{-2(t-3)}u(t-3)$$

Review problems

6   Determine the inverse Laplace transforms of

(a) $\dfrac{s\,e^{-2s}}{s^2+9}$, (b) $\dfrac{3\,e^{-3s}}{s^2+9}$, (c) $\dfrac{e^{-2s}}{s^2}$

2.4 Convolution theorem

If $F_1(s)$ and $F_2(s)$ are the Laplace transforms of $f_1(t)$ and $f_2(t)$ then

$$F_1(s)F_2(s) = \mathcal{L}\left\{\int_0^t f_1(\tau)f_2(t-\tau)\,d\tau\right\} \qquad [5]$$

This product of the two Laplace transforms is termed the *convolution* of the two functions $f_1(t)$ and $f_2(t)$ and is written as

$$F_1(s)F_2(s) = \mathcal{L}\{f_1(t) * f_2(t)\} \qquad [6]$$

and so

$$\mathcal{L}^{-1}\{F_1(s)F_2(s)\} = f_1(t) * f_2(t) \qquad [7]$$

This expression enables the inverse transform of a product of transforms to be obtained.

It should be noted that the inverse Laplace transform of the product of two transforms is *not* equal to the product of the two corresponding time functions.

$$\mathcal{L}^{-1}\{F_1(s)F_2(s)\} \neq f_1(t)f_2(t)$$

Example

Determine the inverse transform of

$$\frac{1}{(s+2)(s+5)}$$

Let $F_1(s) = 1/(s+2)$ and $F_2(s) = 1/(s+5)$, then $f_1(t) = e^{-2t}$ and $f_2(t) = e^{-5t}$. Hence

$$\mathcal{L}^{-1}\left\{\frac{1}{(s+2)(s+5)}\right\} = f_1(t) * f_2(t)$$

$$= \int_0^t e^{-2(t-\tau)}e^{-5\tau}\,d\tau$$

$$= \int_0^t e^{-2t}e^{2\tau}e^{-5\tau}\,d\tau$$

$$= e^{-2t}[-3\,e^{-3\tau}]_0^t$$

$$= 3(e^{-2t} - e^{-3t})$$

Review problems

7 Use the convolution theorem to obtain the inverse transformation of

(a) $\dfrac{1}{s(s^2+4)}$, (b) $\dfrac{2}{(s^2+1)(s^2+1)}$, (c) $\dfrac{1}{(s+1)(s-3)}$

Further problems

8 Determine the inverse Laplace transforms of

(a) $\dfrac{5}{s+10}$, (b) $\dfrac{10}{s^2}$, (c) $\dfrac{6}{s(s+3)}$, (d) $\dfrac{1}{(s+4)(s+5)}$,

(e) $\dfrac{4}{s^2+16}$, (f) $\dfrac{6}{(s-2)^4}$, (g) $\dfrac{2s}{s^2+16}$, (h) $\dfrac{s+40}{(s+25)^2}$,

(i) $\dfrac{s}{(s+1)^2}$, (j) $\dfrac{s+10}{(s-3)(s^2+4)}$, (k) $\dfrac{10s-2}{s^2-s-2}$,

(l) $\dfrac{4(s+6)}{(s^2+5s+6)(s+1)}$, (m) $\dfrac{2\,e^{-5s}}{(s+2)^2}$, (n) $\dfrac{6\,e^{-3s}}{(s-2)^4}$,

(o) $\dfrac{3s+2}{s^3} - \dfrac{s-9}{s^2+9}$, (p) $\dfrac{2}{s+4} + \dfrac{16s}{s^2+16}$,

(q) $\dfrac{1}{s^5} - \dfrac{12}{s^2+4}$, (r) $\dfrac{2s-5}{s^2+4} - \dfrac{3}{4-3s}$

3 Transform of derivatives and integrals

3.1 The transform of derivatives

Later in this chapter the Laplace transform will be used to solve differential equations. In order to do this we need to be able to find the Laplace transform of derivatives of functions. Thus we need to find the value of

$$\mathcal{L}\left\{\frac{d}{dt}f(t)\right\} = \int_0^\infty e^{-st}\frac{d}{dt}\{f(t)\}\,dt$$

Integration by parts is used and e^{-st} is taken to become zero when $t = \infty$. Hence

$$\mathcal{L}\left\{\frac{d}{dt}f(t)\right\} = -f(0) + s\int_0^\infty e^{-st}f(t)\,dt$$

$$= -f(0) + sF(s) \qquad\qquad [1]$$

where $f(0)$ is the value of $f(t)$ when $t = 0$ and $F(s)$ is the Laplace transform of $f(t)$.

If $f(t)$ is a known function of t then equation [1] can be used to obtain its Laplace transform. The following example illustrates this.

Example

Use equation [1] to show that the Laplace transform of 1 is $1/s$.

Let $f(t) = 1$, then $df(t)/dt = 0$ and, since $f(0) = 1$, equation [1] gives

$$\mathcal{L}\left\{\frac{d}{dt}f(t)\right\} = sF(s) - f(0)$$

$$\{0\} = s\mathcal{L}\{1\} - 1$$

Hence

$$\mathcal{L}\{1\} = \frac{1}{s}$$

Example

Determine the Laplace transform of

$$4\frac{dx}{dt} - 3$$

given that $x = 2$ when $t = 0$.

Equation [1] gives

$$\mathcal{L}\left\{\frac{d}{dt}f(t)\right\} = sF(s) - f(0)$$

$$\mathcal{L}\left\{\frac{dx}{dt}\right\} = sX(s) - x(0) = sX(s) - 2$$

Thus the Laplace transform of the expression is

$$4[sX(s) - 2] - \frac{3}{s}$$

Review problems

1   Use equation [1] to show that

   (a) $\mathcal{L}\{t\} = \frac{1}{s^2}$, (b) $\mathcal{L}\{e^{at}\} = \frac{1}{(s-a)}$

2   Determine the Laplace transforms of

   (a) $3\frac{dx}{dt} + 2x$, given that $x = 4$ when $t = 0$,

   (b) $2\frac{dx}{dt} + x$, given that $x = 2$ when $t = 0$.

3.1.1 The transform of second and higher derivatives

For a second derivative

$$\mathcal{L}\left\{\frac{d^2}{dt^2}f(t)\right\} = s^2F(s) - sf(0) - \frac{d}{dt}f(0) \qquad [2]$$

where $f(0)$ is the value of $f(t)$ when $t = 0$ and $df(0)/dt$ is the value of the first derivative of $f(t)$ when $t = 0$.

For a third derivative

$$\mathcal{L}\left\{\frac{d^3}{dt^3}f(t)\right\} = s^3 F(s) - s^2 f(0) - s\frac{d}{dt}f(0) - \frac{d^2}{dt^2}f(0) \qquad [3]$$

where $d^2 f(0)/dt^2$ is the value of the second derivative of $f(t)$ when $t = 0$.

The following is a proof of equation [2]. Integration by parts is used.

$$\mathcal{L}\left\{\frac{d^2}{dt^2}f(t)\right\} = \int_0^\infty e^{-st}\frac{d^2}{dt^2}f(t)\,dt$$

$$= \left[e^{-st}\frac{d}{dt}f(t)\right]_0^\infty + s\int_0^\infty e^{-st}\frac{d}{dt}f(t)\,dt$$

$$= -\frac{d}{dt}f(0) + s[-f(0) + sF(s)]$$

$$= s^2 F(s) - sf(0) - \frac{d}{dt}f(0)$$

Example

Use equation [2] to show that $\mathcal{L}\{\sin\omega t\} = \omega/(s^2 + \omega^2)$.

Let $f(t) = \sin\omega t$, then

$$\frac{d}{dt}f(t) = \omega\cos\omega t$$

and

$$\frac{d^2}{dt^2}f(t) = -\omega^2\sin\omega t$$

Since $f(0) = 0$ and $df(0)/dt = \omega$, then equation [2] gives

$$\mathcal{L}\left\{\frac{d^2}{dt^2}f(t)\right\} = s^2 F(s) - sf(0) - \frac{d}{dt}f(0)$$

$$\mathcal{L}\{-\omega^2\sin\omega t\} = s^2\mathcal{L}\{\sin\omega t\} - 0 - \omega$$

$$-\omega^2\mathcal{L}\{\sin\omega t\} = s^2\mathcal{L}\{\sin\omega t\} - \omega$$

$$\mathcal{L}\{\sin\omega t\} = \frac{\omega}{s^2 + \omega^2}$$

Example

Determine the Laplace transform of

$$\frac{d^2x}{dt^2} + 2x$$

given that $x = 2$ and $dx/dt = 0$ when $t = 0$.

Equation [2] for the second derivative gives

$$\mathcal{L}\left\{ \frac{d^2}{dt^2} f(t) \right\} = s^2 F(s) - sf(0) - \frac{d}{dt} f(0)$$

$$\mathcal{L}\left\{ \frac{d^2x}{dt^2} \right\} = s^2 X(s) - sx(0) - \frac{d}{dt} x(0)$$

$$= s^2 X(s) - 2s - 0$$

Thus the expression has the transform of

$$s^2 X(s) - 2s + 2X(s)$$

Review problems

3   Use equation [2] to show that

$$\mathcal{L}\{\cos \omega t\} = \frac{s}{s^2 + \omega^2}$$

4   Determine the Laplace transforms of

(a) $\dfrac{d^2x}{dt^2} + 2\dfrac{dx}{dt} + 2x$, given $x = 4$ and $\dfrac{dx}{dt} = -1$ when $t = 0$,

(b) $2\dfrac{d^2x}{dt^2} - 3\dfrac{dx}{dt} + x$, given $x = 2$ and $\dfrac{dx}{dt} = -1$ when $t = 0$.

3.2 The transform of integrals

If $F(s)$ is the Laplace transform of $f(t)$ then

$$\mathcal{L}\left\{ \int_0^t f(t)\, dt \right\} = \frac{1}{s} F(s) \qquad\qquad [4]$$

The above equation can be proved as follows. Let

$$g(t) = \int_0^t f(t)\, dt$$

Then we have

$$\frac{d}{dt}g(t) = f(t)$$

Using equation [1] for the first derivative of a function,

$$\mathcal{L}\left\{\frac{d}{dt}g(t)\right\} = sG(s) - g(0)$$

Since $g(0) = 0$ and $G(s)$ is the Laplace transform of $g(t)$ then

$$\mathcal{L}\{f(t)\} = s\,\mathcal{L}\left\{\int_0^t f(t)\,dt\right\}$$

and so

$$\mathcal{L}\left\{\int_0^t f(t)\,dt\right\} = \frac{1}{s}F(s)$$

Example

Determine the Laplace transform of $\int_0^t e^{-t}\,dt$.

Using equation [4],

$$\mathcal{L}\left\{\int_0^t e^{-t}\,dt\right\} = \frac{1}{s}\mathcal{L}\{e^{-t}\} = \frac{1}{s(s+1)}$$

Example

Determine the Laplace transform of

$$\frac{1}{C}\int_0^t i(t)\,dt$$

The above expression is for the voltage across a capacitor of capacitance C. Since

$$\mathcal{L}\left\{\int_0^t f(t)\,dt\right\} = \frac{1}{s}F(s)$$

then the Laplace transform of the expression is

$$\frac{1}{Cs}I(s)$$

Review problems

5   Determine the Laplace transform of

$$\int_0^t e^{-2t} \sin 3t \, dt$$

6   Determine the Laplace transform of

$$L\frac{di}{dt} + Ri + \frac{1}{C}\int_0^t i \, dt$$

given that L, C and R are constants and $i = 0$ when $t = 0$.

3.3 Solving differential equations

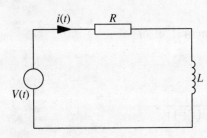

Fig. 3.1 *RL* circuit

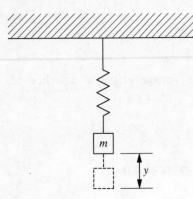

Fig. 3.2 Mass–spring system

Consider the problem of obtaining a mathematical model for the current in the electrical circuit shown in figure 3.1 when the voltage input is some function of time, e.g. a step voltage which involves a steady voltage being abruptly applied at some instant. The voltage drop across the resistor is Ri. The voltage drop across the inductance is $L \, di/dt$. Applying Kirchhoff's voltage law to the circuit gives

$$L\frac{di}{dt} + Ri = V(t)$$

This is a differential equation because it involves the derivative of the current.

Consider a mechanical system consisting of a mass suspended from a spring, as in figure 3.2. The mass is pulled down a distance y and then released. The restoring force acting on the mass is $-ky$, where k is a constant. Applying Newton's second law gives

$$ma = -ky$$

where a is the acceleration. But acceleration is the rate of change of velocity with time and velocity is the rate of change of displacement with time. Thus we can write

$$a = \frac{dv}{dt} = \frac{d}{dt}\left(\frac{dy}{dt}\right) = \frac{d^2 y}{dt^2}$$

Hence we can write for the mathematical model of the mass–spring system

$$m\frac{d^2 y}{dt^2} + ky = 0$$

This is a differential equation because it involves the derivative of the displacement. If instead of just pulling the mass down and releasing it we had applied a force F which was a function of time, then the net restoring force acting on the mass becomes

$$ma - F(t) = ky$$

and so the differential equation describing the motion is

$$m\frac{d^2y}{dt^2} + ky = F(t)$$

The above two examples are intended to illustrate how differential equations frequently arise as mathematical models. The term solution when used with a differential equation describes a function which satisfies the differential equation.

Laplace transforms can be used to solve differential equations. The procedure that is adopted is as follows:

1   Transform each term in the differential equation into its Laplace transform, i.e. put the entire equation into the s-domain.
2   Carry out all algebraic manipulations.
3   Convert the resulting Laplace function back into the time domain, i.e. invert the Laplace transformation operation.

3.3.1 First-order differential equations

The term *first-order* is used for a differential equation which has no derivative greater than the first.

Example

Solve the first-order differential equation

$$3\frac{dx}{dt} + 2x = 4 \text{ with } x = 0 \text{ at } t = 0.$$

The Laplace transform of $3dx/dt$ is given by equation [1] for the transform of the first derivative as

$$3[sX(s) - x(0)] = 3sX(s)$$

The Laplace transform of $2x$ is $2X(s)$. The Laplace transform of 4 is, since this can be considered to be a step function of height 4, $4/s$. Thus

$$3sX(s) + 2X(s) = \frac{4}{s}$$

This can be written as

$$X(s) = \frac{4}{s(3s+2)} = 2\frac{\frac{2}{3}}{s\left(s+\frac{2}{3}\right)}$$

Table 1.1, item 8, gives the inverse transformation

$$\mathcal{L}^{-1}\left\{\frac{a}{s(s+a)}\right\} = 1 - e^{-at}$$

and so the solution of the differential equation is

$$x = 2(1 - e^{-2t/3})$$

Example

For a voltage step input of size V at $t = 0$ into a series CR circuit the differential equation for the potential difference v_C across the capacitor is given by

$$RC\frac{dv_C}{dt} + v_C = V$$

v_C is zero at $t = 0$. Use Laplace transforms to solve the equation.

The Laplace transform of a unit step input is $1/s$ and thus for one of size V it is V/s. For dv_C/dt it is $[sV_C(s) - v_C(0)] = sV_C(s)$. Thus the Laplace transform for $RC\ dv_C/dt$ is $RCsV_C(s)$. The transform of v_C is $V_C(s)$. Thus the transform of the differential equation is

$$RCsV_C(s) + V_C(s) = \frac{V}{s}$$

This can be written as

$$V_C(s) = \frac{V}{s(RCs+1)} = V\frac{(1/RC)}{s(s+1/RC)}$$

Table 1.1, item 8, gives the inverse transform of $a/s(s + a)$ as $(1 - e^{-at})$. Thus, with $a = 1/RC$, then the differential equation has the solution

$$v_C = V(1 - e^{-t/RC})$$

The term *time constant* is used for the product RC.

Example

When a mercury-in-glass thermometer is inserted into a hot liquid there is essentially a step input of temperature to the thermometer. Let θ_i be the temperature of the hot liquid. The rate at which the thermometer temperature changes is proportional to the difference in temperatures between the thermometer and the liquid. The relationship between the output of the thermometer θ_o, i.e. its reading, and time is thus given by the first-order differential equation

$$K\frac{d\theta_o}{dt} = \theta_i - \theta_o$$

or

$$K\frac{d\theta_o}{dt} + \theta_o = \theta_i$$

where θ_o is a function of time. Use the Laplace transformation to obtain a solution for this equation. Take the value of θ_o to be 0 at $t = 0$, i.e. in this problem we are only concerned with the change in temperature when the thermometer is inserted into the liquid. θ_o is thus the temperature of the hot liquid relative to that of the thermometer before it is inserted into the liquid.

The Laplace transform of $d\theta_o/dt$ is $[s\Theta_o(s) - 0]$, since the value of θ_o is 0 at $t = 0$. Thus the transform for $K d\theta_o/dt$ is $Ks\Theta_o(s)$. The transform of is θ_i is θ_i/s since it is a step input, and that of θ_o is $\Theta_o(s)$. Hence the transform of the differential equation is

$$Ks\Theta_o(s) + \Theta_o(s) = \frac{\theta_i}{s}$$

This can be rearranged to give

$$\Theta_o(s) = \frac{\theta_i}{s(Ks + 1)} = \theta_i\frac{(1/K)}{s(s + 1/K)}$$

This is of the same form as item 8 in table 1.1 and thus the inverse transform, and hence the solution of the differential equation, is

$$\theta_o = \theta_i(1 - e^{-t/K})$$

Example

A series CR circuit has an input of a ramp voltage Vt, where V is the voltage rise per second. The potential difference across the capacitor v_C is a function of time and described by the following differential equation:

$$RC\frac{dv_C}{dt} + v_C = Vt$$

When $t = 0$ then $v_C = 0$. Solve the differential equation.

The Laplace transform of the equation gives

$$RCV_C(s) + RCv_C(0) + V_C = \frac{V}{s^2}$$

Hence

$$V_C(s) = \frac{V}{s^2(RCs+1)} = V\frac{(1/RC)}{s^2(s+1/RC)}$$

Item 11 in table 1.1 gives the inverse transform of $a/s^2(s+a)$ as $t - (1 - e^{-at})/a$ and hence

$$v_C = Vt - VRC(1 - e^{-t/RC})$$

Review problems

7 Solve the differential equations

(a) $\dfrac{dx}{dt} + 5x = 2$, with $x = 0$ when $t = 0$,

(b) $3\dfrac{dx}{dt} + 2x = 5$, with $x = 0$ when $t = 0$.

8 For a step input at $t = 0$ of size V into a series LR circuit the current variation with time is described by the equation

$$\frac{L}{R}\frac{di}{dt} + i = \frac{V}{R}$$

The current i is zero at $t = 0$. Using Laplace transforms solve this equation.

9 Solve the differential equations

(a) $4\dfrac{dx}{dt} + 3x = 2t$, with $x = 0$ when $t = 0$,

(b) $2\dfrac{dx}{dt} + x = 4e^{2t}$, with $x = 0$ when $t = 0$,

(c) $\dfrac{dx}{dt} + x = t^2e^{-t}$, with $x = 1$ when $t = 0$.

3.3.2 Second-order differential equations

Second-order differential equations contain the second derivative of a function as the highest derivative.

Example

Solve the second-order differential equation

$$\frac{d^2x}{dt^2} + 9x = 0 \text{ with } x = 0 \text{ and } \frac{dx}{dt} = 3 \text{ when } t = 0.$$

The Laplace transform for the differential equation is

$$s^2 X(s) - sx(0) - \frac{d}{dt}x(0) + 9X(s) = 0$$

Hence

$$X(s) = \frac{3}{s^2 + 9}$$

Item 16 in table 1.1 gives the inverse transform of $\omega/(s^2 + \omega^2)$ as $\sin \omega t$, hence

$$x = \sin 3t$$

Example

Solve the second order differential equation

$$\frac{d^2x}{dt^2} + x = t, \text{ with } x = 0 \text{ and } \frac{dx}{dt} = 2 \text{ when } t = 0.$$

The Laplace transform for the differential equation is

$$s^2 X(s) - sx(0) - \frac{d}{dt}x(0) + X(s) = \frac{1}{s^2}$$

Hence

$$X(s) = \frac{1}{s^2(s^2 + 1)} + \frac{2}{s^2 + 1}$$

Partial fractions can be used to simplify the first fractional term.

$$X(s) = \frac{1}{s^2} - \frac{1}{s^2 + 1} + \frac{2}{s^2 + 1} = \frac{1}{s^2} + \frac{1}{s^2 + 1}$$

The inverse transform is thus

$$x = t + \sin t$$

Review problems

10 Solve the differential equations

(a) $\dfrac{d^2x}{dt^2} + 3\dfrac{dx}{dt} + 2x = 0$ with $x = 0$ and $\dfrac{dx}{dt} = 2$ at $t = 0$,

(b) $\dfrac{d^2x}{dt^2} + 3\dfrac{dx}{dt} + 2x = 4\,e^{-3t}$ with $x = 2$ and $\dfrac{dx}{dt} = -1$ at $t = 0$,

(c) $\dfrac{d^2x}{dt^2} - 3\dfrac{dx}{dt} + 2x = 6\,e^{-t}$ with $x = 3$ and $\dfrac{dx}{dt} = 3$ at $t = 0$,

(d) $\dfrac{d^2x}{dt^2} - 2\dfrac{dx}{dt} - 8x = 4$ with $x = 0$ and $\dfrac{dx}{dt} = 1$ at $t = 0$,

(e) $\dfrac{d^2x}{dt^2} + 4\dfrac{dx}{dt} + 4x = \sin t$ with $x = 2$ and $\dfrac{dx}{dt} = 0$ at $t = 0$.

11 A particle which is describing simple harmonic motion has an acceleration a which is related to the displacement x by

$$a = \frac{d^2x}{dt^2} = -4x$$

with $x = 10$ and $dx/dt = 0$ when $t = 0$. Solve the differential equation.

12 The motion described in the previous question was undamped. With damping taken into consideration the equation becomes

$$a = \frac{d^2x}{dt^2} = -4x - 4\frac{dx}{dt}$$

with the same initial conditions as above. Solve the differential equation.

3.4 Simultaneous differential equations

A set of simultaneous equations can arise when Kirchhoff's laws are applied to networks containing capacitors and/or inductors and resistors. A differential equation can be written for each mesh or node. Similar sets of differential equations can arise when the vibration of a mechanical system involving two masses is considered.

A set of simultaneous differential equations can be solved by:

1   Transforming each differential equation into its Laplace transform.
2   Solve the resulting simultaneous equations using the conventional methods for algebraic simultaneous equations.
3   Convert the resulting Laplace functions back into equations giving them as functions of time, i.e. invert them.

Example

Solve the simultaneous equations

$$\frac{dx}{dt} + x - 3y = 0 \text{ and } \frac{dy}{dt} + 3x - y = e^{-t}$$

when $x = 0$ and $y = 0$ at $t = 0$.

The transformed equations are

$$sX(s) + X(s) - 3Y(s) = 0$$

$$sY(s) + 3X(s) - Y(s) = \frac{1}{s+1}$$

These equations can be written in the form

$$(s+1)X(s) - 3Y(s) = 0$$

$$3X(s) + (s-1)Y(s) = \frac{1}{s+1}$$

$X(s)$ can be eliminated by multiplying the first equation by 3 and the second equation by $(s+1)$, then subtracting one from the other.

$$-9Y(s) - (s+1)(s-1)Y(s) = -1$$

Hence

$$Y(s) = \frac{1}{9 + (s+1)(s-1)}$$

$$= \frac{1}{s^2 + 8}$$

The inverse of this can be obtained by the use of item 16 in table 1.1, thus

$$y = \frac{1}{\sqrt{8}} \sin \sqrt{8}\, t$$

We can substitute the above value of $Y(s)$ into a transformed equation and so obtain $X(s)$. Thus

$$(s+1)X(s) = 3Y(s) = \frac{3}{s^2 + 8}$$

$$X(s) = \frac{3}{(s+1)(s^2 + 8)}$$

Partial fractions can then be used to put the equation into a suitable form for inversion.

An alternative, and often simpler, method is to substitute for y into one of the differential equations. Thus

$$\frac{dy}{dt} + 3x - y = e^{-t}$$

$$\cos \sqrt{8}\, t + 3x - \frac{1}{\sqrt{8}} \sin \sqrt{8}\, t = e^{-t}$$

and so

$$x = \frac{1}{3} e^{-t} + \frac{1}{3\sqrt{8}} \sin \sqrt{8}\, t - \frac{1}{3} \cos \sqrt{8}\, t$$

Review problems

13   Solve the simultaneous differential equations

(a) $\dfrac{dx}{dt} - 2x + 3y = 0$ and $\dfrac{dy}{dt} + 2x - y = 0$

with $x = 0$ and $y = 0$ when $t = 0$,

(b) $\dfrac{dx}{dt} - x - 2y = 0$ and $\dfrac{dy}{dt} - 3x + 4y = 0$

with $x = 0$ and $y = 1$ when $t = 0$,

(c) $\dfrac{dx}{dt} + 2\dfrac{dy}{dt} + 2y = 0$ and $2\dfrac{dx}{dt} + \dfrac{dy}{dt} + 2x = 2$

with $x = 0$ and $y = 0$ when $t = 0$,

(d) $\dfrac{dx}{dt} + 4\dfrac{dy}{dt} + 3y = 0$ and $3\dfrac{dx}{dt} + \dfrac{dy}{dt} + 2x = 1$

with $x = 0$ and $y = 0$ when $t = 0$.

3.5 Initial and final value theorems

The initial value of a function is the value at a time $t = 0$, the final value is the value at $t = \infty$. Thus, for example, if we consider an *LR* circuit then if there is a step input the circuit current will change with time and eventually reach a steady value. This steady value can be considered to be the current attained as the time t tends to an infinite value. Thus the final value of a function is the steady state value attained after all transients have ceased.

The initial and final value theorems are useful because they enable the behaviour of $f(t)$ at $t = 0$ and $t = \infty$ to be determined from $F(s)$ without the need to find the inverse transform of $F(s)$.

3.5.1 The initial value theorem

The *initial value theorem* can be stated as: if a function of time $f(t)$ has a Laplace transform $F(s)$ then in the limit as the time tends to zero the value of the function is given by

$$\lim_{t \to 0} f(t) = \lim_{s \to \infty} sF(s) \qquad [5]$$

This can be proved as follows. Since we have, by definition (see section 1.1),

$$\mathcal{L}\{f(t)\} = \int_0^\infty e^{-st} f(t)\, dt$$

then

$$\mathcal{L}\left\{\frac{d}{dt} f(t)\right\} = \int_0^\infty e^{-st} \frac{d}{dt} f(t)\, dt \qquad [6]$$

This can be integrated by parts to give

$$\mathcal{L}\left\{\frac{d}{dt} f(t)\right\} = [e^{-st} f(t)]_0^\infty - \int_0^\infty (-s\,e^{-st}) f(t)\, dt$$

$$= -f(0) + sF(s) \qquad [7]$$

As s tends to infinity then e^{-st} will tend to zero and thus

$$\lim_{s \to \infty} \int_0^\infty e^{-st} \frac{d}{dt} f(t)\, dt = 0$$

Hence

$$\lim_{s \to \infty} [-f(0) + sF(s)] = 0$$

and so

$$\lim_{s \to \infty} sF(s) = f(0) = \lim_{t \to 0} f(t)$$

Example

Determine the initial value of the function $5\,e^{-2t}$.

For the function

$$F(s) = \frac{5}{s+2}$$

Hence applying the initial value theorem

$$\lim_{t\to 0}\,[5e^{-2t}] = \lim_{s\to\infty}\left[\frac{5s}{s+2}\right]$$

$$= \lim_{s\to\infty}\left[\frac{5}{1+2/s}\right] = 5$$

The initial value is thus 5. We could have obtained this directly from the function since $5\,e^{-0} = 5$.

Example

Determine the initial value of $f(t)$ when

$$F(s) = \frac{3s+2}{s^2+2s+1}$$

Using the initial value theorem

$$\lim_{t\to 0}\,[f(t)] = \lim_{s\to\infty}\left[\frac{s(3s+2)}{s^2+2s+1}\right]$$

$$= \lim_{s\to\infty}\left[\frac{s^2(3+2/s)}{s^2(1+2/s+1/s^2)}\right] = 3$$

Review problems

14   Determine the initial values of $f(t)$ when

(a) $F(s) = \dfrac{4}{s^2-3s+1}$, (b) $F(s) = \dfrac{4s+1}{s^2-2s+1}$

15   Verify the initial value theorem for the functions
(a) $4 - 2\cos t$, (b) $(2t+1)^2$.

3.5.2 The final value theorem

The *final value theorem* can be stated as: if a function of time $f(t)$ has a Laplace transform $F(s)$ then in the limit as the time tends to infinity the value of the function is given by

$$\lim_{t \to \infty} f(t) = \lim_{s \to 0} sF(s) \qquad [8]$$

This can be proved as follows. Considering the function given above as equation [6], and the results of integration by parts as equation [7], then we can write

$$\mathcal{L}\left\{\frac{d}{dt}f(t)\right\} = -f(0) + sF(s)$$

As s tends to zero then e^{-st} tends to 1. Thus

$$\lim_{s \to 0} \int_0^\infty e^{-st} \frac{d}{dt}f(t)\,dt = \int_0^\infty \frac{d}{dt}f(t)\,dt$$

But

$$\int_0^\infty \frac{d}{dt}f(t)\,dt = \lim_{t \to \infty} \int_0^t \frac{d}{dt}f(t)\,dt$$

$$= \lim_{t \to \infty} [f(t) - f(0)]$$

Hence

$$\lim_{s \to 0} [sF(s) - f(0)] = \lim_{t \to \infty} [f(t) - f(0)]$$

and so

$$\lim_{s \to 0} sF(s) = \lim_{t \to \infty} f(t)$$

Care must be taken in using this theorem since a function may not have a final value as the time tends to an infinite value. There will only be a finite value at infinity if s has real values. Thus it cannot be applied to the function $f(s) = \sin \omega t$. The theorem would imply that

$$\lim_{s \to 0} sF(s) = \lim_{s \to 0} \left[\frac{s\omega}{s^2 + \omega^2} \right] = 0$$

which is not the case.

Example

Determine the final value of $f(t)$ when

$$F(s) = \frac{2s + 5}{s^2 + 3s + 1}.$$

Using the final value theorem

$$\lim_{t\to\infty} f(t) = \lim_{s\to 0} sF(s) = \lim_{s\to 0}\left[\frac{s(2s+5)}{s^2+3s+1}\right] = 0$$

Review problems

16 Determine the final value of $f(t)$ when

$$(a)\ F(s) = \frac{4s+1}{s^2+2s+1},\ (b)\ F(s) = \frac{s^2+2}{s(s+1)(s+2)}$$

Further problems

17 Solve the differential equations

(a) $\dfrac{dx}{dt} - 2x = 3$ with $x = 0$ when $t = 0$,

(b) $2\dfrac{dx}{dt} - 2x + t = 0$ with $x = 2$ when $t = 0$,

(c) $\dfrac{dx}{dt} - 3x = 13\sin 2t$ with $x = 0$ when $t = 0$,

(d) $\dfrac{dx}{dt} + 4x = 1$ with $x = 2$ when $t = 0$,

(e) $\dfrac{dx}{dt} + 4x = \cos t$ with $x = 0$ when $t = 0$.

18 Solve the differential equations

(a) $\dfrac{d^2x}{dt^2} + 2\dfrac{dx}{dt} + 5x = \sin 2t$ with $x = 0$ and $\dfrac{dx}{dt} = 0$ when $t = 0$,

(b) $\dfrac{d^2x}{dt^2} + 2\dfrac{dx}{dt} + x = 6\cos t$ with $x = 0$ and $\dfrac{dx}{dt} = 0$ when $t = 0$,

(c) $\dfrac{d^2x}{dt^2} + 3\dfrac{dx}{dt} + 2x = e^{-t}$ with $x = 0$ and $\dfrac{dx}{dt} = 0$ when $t = 0$,

(d) $\dfrac{d^2x}{dt^2} + 4\dfrac{dx}{dt} + 5x = 5$ with $x = 1$ and $\dfrac{dx}{dt} = 1$ when $t = 0$,

(e) $\dfrac{d^2x}{dt^2} + 4\dfrac{dx}{dt} + 4x = 0$ with $x = 0$ and $\dfrac{dx}{dt} = 2$ when $t = 0$.

19   Solve the simultaneous equations

(a) $\dfrac{dx}{dt} + 2x + y = 0$ and $\dfrac{dx}{dt} + x + 2y = 0$

with $x = 1$ and $y = 0$ when $t = 0$,

(b) $\dfrac{dx}{dt} + y = \sin t$ and $\dfrac{dy}{dt} + x = \cos t$

with $x = 2$ and $y = 0$ when $t = 0$,

(c) $\dfrac{dx}{dt} + 3x - 2y = 1$ and $\dfrac{dy}{dt} - 2x + 3y = e^t$

with $x = 0$ and $y = 0$ when $t = 0$.

20   An electrical circuit consists of a resistance R, an inductance L and a capacitance C in series and the mathematical model describing how the current i varies with time is

$$L\dfrac{d^2 i}{dt^2} + R\dfrac{di}{dt} + \dfrac{1}{C}i = 0$$

At time $t = 0$ the initially charged capacitor gives rise to a rate of change of current di/dt of 40 mA/s. If the initial current is zero, solve the differential equation for a circuit which has inductance 0.20 H, resistance 200 Ω and capacitance 25 μF.

21   An electrical circuit consists of a resistance R in series with an inductance L. At time $t = 0$ a constant voltage V is abruptly applied to the series arrangement. The mathematical model for the system is

$$L\dfrac{di}{dt} + Ri = Vu(t)$$

If the current is zero at $t = 0$, solve the differential equation.

22   An electrical circuit consists of a resistance R in series with an inductance L. At time $t = 0$ a sinusoidal voltage 5 sin t is applied to the series arrangement. For a resistance of 5 Ω and an inductance of 5 H the mathematical model is

$$5\dfrac{di}{dt} + 5i = 5 \sin t$$

If the current is zero at $t = 0$, solve the differential equation.

23   An electrical circuit consists of a resistance R in series with an inductance L. At time $t = 5$ s a constant voltage of 2 V is

applied to the series arrangement. Up to that time the applied voltage is zero. The mathematical model for the system is

$$L\frac{di}{dt} + Ri = 2u(t-5)$$

If the current is zero at $t = 0$, solve the differential equation.

24 An electrical circuit consists of a resistance R in series with a capacitance C. At time $t = 0$ a constant voltage of 10 V is applied to the series arrangement. Up to that time the applied voltage was zero and the charge on the capacitor zero. The mathematical model for the system is

$$R\frac{dq}{dt} + \frac{1}{C}q = Vu(t)$$

If $R = 25$ kΩ and $C = 1$ μF, solve the differential equation.

25 What would the answer to problem 24 be if the constant voltage had not been applied at $t = 0$ but at $t = 3$ s?

26 A series electrical circuit consists of a resistance R, a capacitance C and an inductance L. At time $t = 0$ an impulse of size 1 V is applied to the circuit. Up to that time the charge on the capacitor was zero and the circuit current was zero. The mathematical model for the system is

$$L\frac{d^2q}{dt^2} + R\frac{dq}{dt} + \frac{1}{C}q = \delta(t)$$

If $L = 1$ H, $R = 10$ Ω and $C = 0.01$ F, solve the differential equation.

27 An object oscillates with simple harmonic motion such that the displacement x is related to the acceleration a by the equation

$$a = \frac{d^2x}{dt^2} = -16x$$

with $x = 3$ and $dx/dt = 16$ when $t = 0$. Solve the equation.

28 An oscillating object is subject to a unit force which lasts from $t = 0$ to $t = 1$ s and has a displacement x which is given by

$$\frac{d^2x}{dt^2} + 3\frac{dx}{dt} + 2x = u(t) - u(t-1)$$

If $x = 0$ and $dx/dt = 0$ at $t = 0$, solve the differential equation.

29   Determine the initial and final values of $f(t)$ for

$$\text{(a) } F(s) = \frac{3s+7}{s^2+4s+6}, \text{ (b) } F(s) = \frac{5s+20}{s(s+2)}$$

30   Verify that the initial value theorem applies to the function $f(t) = e^t + \cos t$.

31   Verify that the final value theorem applies to the function $f(t) = t^3 e^{-2t}$.

32   A series LR circuit has

$$I(s) = \frac{s+2}{s(s+1)}$$

What are the initial and final values of the current?

33   A series LCR circuit has

$$I(s) = \frac{5}{(s+1)(s+2)}$$

What are the initial and final values of the current?

34   A series LCR circuit has

$$V_C(s) = \frac{2(s^2+3s+3)}{s(s+1)(s+2)}$$

What are the initial and final values of the voltage across the capacitor v_c?

4 Electrical circuits in the s-domain

4.1 Circuit elements in the s-domain

In the time domain the terminal characteristic of a circuit element, such as a resistor, capacitor or inductor, is expressed in terms of the relationship between voltage and current at the terminals of the element, e.g. for a resistance we have $V = RI$. In a similar way we can express the terminal characteristic in the s-domain in terms of the relationship between the transformed voltage and the transformed current.

Impedance in the s-domain $Z(s)$ is defined as

$$Z(s) = \frac{V(s)}{I(s)} \tag{1}$$

The unit of the impedance is the ohm. The reciprocal of impedance is admittance, therefore *admittance* in the s-domain $Y(s)$ is

$$Y(s) = \frac{I(s)}{V(s)} \tag{2}$$

The unit of the admittance is the siemen (S).

4.1.1 Resistor transformation

For a *resistor* the relationship between the potential difference v across it at some instant of time and the current i through it, when both are functions of time, is

$$v(t) = Ri(t)$$

or, as usually written with the functions of time being understood, $v = Ri$. R is the resistance and is a constant that does not change with time. The Laplace transform of the equation is thus

$$V(s) = RI(s)$$

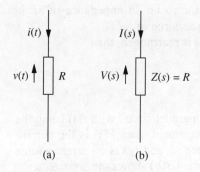

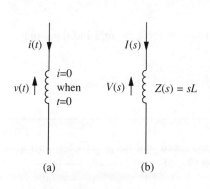

Fig. 4.1 The resistor element (a) in the time domain, (b) in the s-domain

where $V(s)$ is the transform of the potential difference and $I(s)$ the transform of the current. So in the s-domain if we define resistance $R(s)$ as $V(s)/I(s)$, then

$$R(s) = \frac{V(s)}{I(s)} = R \qquad [3]$$

Thus the s-domain equivalent circuit of a resistor is a resistance of R that has a current $I(s)$ and a potential difference $V(s)$ (figure 4.1).

4.1.2 Inductor transformation

For an *inductor* with no initial current, i.e. $i = 0$ at $t = 0$, the equation relating the potential difference v across it with the rate of change of current is

$$v = L\frac{di}{dt}$$

with both v and i being functions of time. L is the inductance, a constant that does not vary with time. The Laplace transform of the equation is

$$V(s) = L[sI(s) - i(0)]$$

and as $i(0) = 0$ then

$$V(s) = sLI(s)$$

The impedance $Z(s)$ of the inductor in the s-domain of the inductor can be considered to be $V(s)/I(s)$. Thus

$$Z(s) = \frac{V(s)}{I(s)} = sL \qquad [4]$$

Thus in the s-domain the equivalent circuit of an inductor is an impedance of sL (figure 4.2).

If, for the inductor, instead of the current being zero at $t = 0$ but some value i_0, then the transform would be

$$V(s) = L[sI(s) - i(0)] = sLI(s) - Li_0 \qquad [5]$$

Since sL is the impedance in the s-domain of the inductor then the potential difference in the s-domain across it is $sLI(s)$. Thus the equation can be considered to describe two series elements with

$$V(s) = \text{p.d. across } L + \text{voltage generator of } (-Li_0) \qquad [6]$$

Fig. 4.2 The inductor element (a) in the time domain, (b) in the s-domain

We can consider such an inductor to be an impedance of sL in series with an independent voltage source of $-Li_0$.

Alternatively, if equation [5] is rearranged, then

$$I(s) = \frac{V(s) + LI_0}{sL} = \frac{V(s)}{sL} + \frac{i_0}{s}$$

If we consider this to represent a parallel circuit with $I(s)$ being the current entering the parallel arrangement, then $V(s)$ is the current through the inductor of impedance sL and i_0/s is a current source in parallel with the inductor. Figure 4.3(b) shows the arrangement.

$$I(s) = \text{current through } L \text{ plus current source } i_0/s \qquad [7]$$

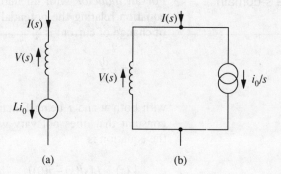

Fig. 4.3 The inductor element in the s-domain with current i_0 at $t = 0$, (a) series equivalent circuit, (b) parallel equivalent circuit

Example

What is the impedance in the s-domain of a 1 mH inductance?

Using equation [4]

$$Z(s) = sL = 0.001s\,\Omega$$

Example

What is the parallel transformed model for a 50 mH inductor that has a current of 0.1 A at $t = 0$?

The transformed impedance is given by equation [4] as

$$Z(s) = sL = 0.050s\,\Omega$$

With the parallel model, this impedance will be in parallel with a current source, given by equation [7], of

$$\frac{i_0}{s} = \frac{0.1}{s} \text{ A s}$$

Note that the unit is A s. This is because s has the dimensional equivalent of 1/second, i.e. s^{-1}. However, the time element of the unit is very often omitted.

Review problems

1   Determine the series and parallel models in the *s*-domain for an inductor with 50 mH inductance that has a current of 0.2 A at the time $t = 0$.
2   Determine the series and parallel models in the *s*-domain for an inductor with 1 mH inductance that has a current of 2 mA at the time $t = 0$.

4.1.3 Capacitor transformation

For a *capacitor* with no initial potential difference

$$i = C\frac{dv}{dt}$$

where the current i and the potential difference v are functions of time. C is the capacitance. The Laplace transform of this equation is

$$I(s) = C[sV(s) - v(0)]$$

Since we have the condition that $v(0) = 0$ then the impedance of the capacitor in the *s*-domain is

$$Z(s) = \frac{V(s)}{I(s)} = \frac{1}{sC} \qquad [8]$$

Figure 4.4 illustrates this.

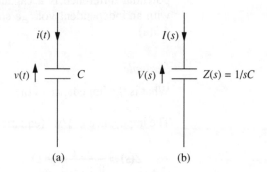

Fig. 4.4 The capacitor element (a) in the time domain, (b) in the *s*-domain

If the capacitor has an initial potential difference v_0 at $t = 0$, then

$$I(s) = C[sV(s) - v(0)] = CsV(s) - Cv_0 \qquad [9]$$

Since $V(s)/(1/sC) = CsV(s)$ is the current through the capacitor, equation [9] can represent a parallel circuit with

$$I(s) = \text{current through } C + \text{current source } (-Cv_0) \qquad [10]$$

An equivalent circuit is thus a capacitor of impedance $1/sC$ in parallel with an independent current source of $-Cv_0$, as illustrated in figure 4.5(b).

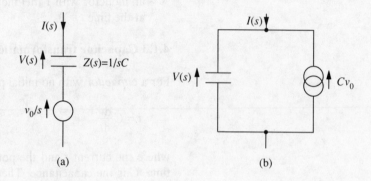

Fig. 4.5 The capacitor element in the s-domain with potential difference v_0 at $t = 0$, (a) series equivalent circuit, (b) parallel equivalent circuit

As an alternative we can rearrange equation [9] to give

$$V(s) = \frac{1}{sC} I(s) + \frac{v_0}{s} \qquad [11]$$

and thus for a series arrangement of capacitor and a voltage source

$$V(s) = \text{p.d. across } C + \text{voltage source } v_0/s \qquad [12]$$

An equivalent circuit in the s-domain for a capacitor with an initial potential difference is a capacitor with impedance $1/sC$ in series with an independent voltage source of v_0/s, as illustrated in figure 4.5(a).

Example

What is the impedance in the s-domain of a 0.1 µF capacitor?

The impedance is $1/sC$ (equation [8]) and thus

$$Z(s) = \frac{1}{0.1 \times 10^{-6} s} \, \Omega$$

Example

What is the series transformed model for a 2 µF capacitor that has been charged to a voltage of 6 V at $t = 0$?

The impedance is given by equation [8] as

$$Z(s) = \frac{1}{sC} = \frac{1}{2 \times 10^{-6}s} \; \Omega$$

This will be in series with a voltage source, given by equation [12] as

$$\frac{v_0}{s} = \frac{6}{s} \; \text{V s}$$

Note the unit of V s, this is because *s* has the dimensional effect of /second. Often, however, the time element of the transformed unit is omitted.

Review problems

3   Determine the series and parallel transformed models for a capacitor of 2 μF capacitance that has been charged to 5 V at the time *t* = 0.

4.1.4 Complex frequency domain

A point to notice is the similarity between the impedance, or admittance, expressions in the *s*-domain and the expressions obtained for sinusoidal signals using complex numbers, i.e. *s* is similar to jω. Thus, for example, in the *s*-domain for a capacitor $Z(s) = 1/sC$ while using complex numbers $Z = 1/j\omega C$. For this reason *s* is sometimes called the *complex frequency* and the *s*-domain as the *complex frequency domain*.

4.2 Circuits in the s-domain

Kirchhoff's laws are applicable to *s*-domain currents and voltages in exactly the same way as they are used with time-domain currents and voltages. This is because the Laplace transform of the sum of a number of time-domain functions is the sum of the transforms of each function treated independently. Thus, for Kirchhoff's current law in the time domain the sum of the currents at a junction is zero. For each current we can obtain the Laplace transform and thus the sum of the transformed currents is also zero. Similarly for Kirchhoff's voltage law in the time domain the sum of the voltages around a closed loop is zero and thus the sum of the voltages in the s-domain is also zero.

A consequence of being able to apply Kirchhoff's laws to currents and voltages in the *s*-domain is that all the techniques of circuit analysis developed for time-domain circuits apply to *s*-domain circuits. Thus, for example, the rules for combining impedances, or admittances, in the s-domain are exactly the same as those used in the time domain. Thévenin's theorem, Norton's theorem, the superposition theorem, the methods of node analysis and mesh analysis can all be used in the s-domain.

4.2.1 Combining impedances and admittances

In the s-domain the total impedance $Z(s)$ of a number of impedances in series is the sum, i.e.

$$Z(s) = Z_1(s) + Z_2(s) + \dots \qquad [13]$$

The total impedance of a number of impedances in parallel is

$$\frac{1}{Z(s)} = \frac{1}{Z_1(s)} + \frac{1}{Z_2(s)} + \dots \qquad [14]$$

Example

What is the impedance in the s-domain of a 100 Ω resistor in series with a 4 mH inductor?

The impedance in the s-domain of the resistor is 100 Ω, while that of the inductor is $sL = 4 \times 10^{-3} s \, \Omega$. For two impedances in series the total impedance is their sum, hence

$$Z(s) = 100 + 4 \times 10^{-3} s \, \Omega$$

Example

What is the admittance in the s-domain of a 100 Ω resistor, a 4 mH inductor and a 0.1 μF capacitor in parallel?

The admittance in the s-domain of the resistor is $1/R = 0.01$ S, that of the inductor $1/sL = 1/(4 \times 10^{-3} s) = 250/s$, and that of the capacitor $sC = 0.1 \times 10^{-6} s$ S. The total admittance is the sum of the three admittances and so is

$$0.01 + \frac{250}{s} + 0.1 \times 10^{-6} s \text{ S}$$

Review problems

4   Determine the impedance in the s-domain of
    (a) 10 Ω in series with 50 Ω,
    (b) 10 Ω in series with an inductance of 2 mH,
    (c) 10 Ω in series with a 8 μF capacitance,
    (d) 10 Ω in parallel with 20 Ω,
    (e) 10 Ω in parallel with an inductance of 2 mH,

(f) 10 Ω in parallel with a 8 μF capacitance.
5   Determine the admittance in the s-domain of
(a) 20 Ω in parallel with an inductance of 0.5 H,
(b) a capacitance of 10 μF in parallel with an inductance of
0.5 H.

4.2.2 Combining ideal sources

In the s-domain voltage sources in series can be combined by
algebraic addition and then replaced by a single equivalent source.
Current sources in parallel are combined by algebraic addition and
can then be replaced by a single equivalent source.

Example

Determine the total current source in the s-domain when there are
two parallel current sources of 4 A and 4/s A.

The total current source is the sum of the two parallel current
sources and so is 4 + 4/s A.

Example

Determine the single equivalent voltage source when, in the
s-domain, a circuit has voltage sources of 6 V and $3/s^2$ V in series.

The equivalent source is the sum of the two series voltage sources
and so is 6 + $3/s^2$ V.

Review problems

6   What is the equivalent voltage source in the s-domain when
there are voltage sources of 2 V and 3/(s + 2) V in series?
7   What is the equivalent current source in the s-domain when
there are current sources of 0.5 A and 2/s A in parallel?

4.2.3 Determination of time function

The procedure for the solution of circuits in the s-domain is:

1   Convert the time-domain circuit to one in the s-domain.
2   Apply the circuit laws and write down the equation or
equations for the circuit for the elements in the s-domain.
3   Solve the equations to obtain the Laplace transform of the
required quantity.
4   Rearrange the equations into a form that can be recognised in
the table of Laplace transforms.
5   Hence obtain the inverse transformation and so the solution.

Example

Derive an expression for the variation with time of the current in a circuit consisting of a resistor R in series with an initially uncharged capacitor C when the input to the circuit is a step voltage of size V at the time $t = 0$.

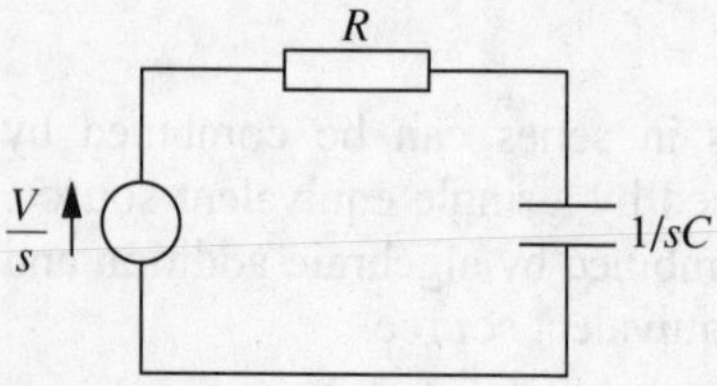

The circuit in the s-domain is as shown in figure 4.6, the step voltage being V/s, the impedance of the capacitor $1/sC$ and the resistance R. The voltage across each component will be the product of their impedance and the current, both being in the s-domain. Thus applying Kirchhoff's voltage law to the circuit gives

$$\frac{V}{s} = RI(s) + \frac{1}{sC}I(s)$$

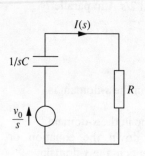

Fig. 4.6 Example

Thus

$$I(s) = \frac{V}{Rs + 1/C} = V\frac{(1/R)}{s + (1/RC)}$$

This is of the form $1/(s+a)$, for which the inverse transform is e^{-at}. Thus

$$i = \frac{V}{R}e^{-t/RC}$$

Example

A charged capacitor, with a potential difference v_0, is suddenly discharged through a resistor. Determine how the current varies with time.

The charged capacitor can be represented by a generator of voltage v_0/s in series with an impedance $1/sC$ (equation [12]). Figure 4.7 shows the circuit. Applying Kirchhoff's voltage law to the circuit gives

$$\frac{v_0}{s} = \frac{I(s)}{sC} + RI(s)$$

Hence, after rearrangement,

$$I(s) = \frac{v_0}{sR + 1/C} = \frac{v_0/R}{s + 1/RC}$$

Fig. 4.7 Example

This is of the form $1/(s + a)$ with $a = 1/RC$. Thus the inverse transform is

$$i = \frac{v_0}{R} e^{-t/RC}$$

Example

A ramp voltage of $v = kt$ is applied at $t = 0$ to a circuit consisting of an inductance L in series with a resistance R. If initially at $t = 0$ there is no current, derive an expression for how the current varies with time t.

In the *s*-domain a unit ramp voltage of $1t$ is $1/s^2$ and thus a ramp of kt is k/s^2. The inductance has an impedance in the *s*-domain of sL and the resistance one of R. Figure 4.8 shows the circuit in the *s*-domain. Thus applying Kirchhoff's voltage law

$$\frac{k}{s^2} = sLI(s) + RI(s)$$

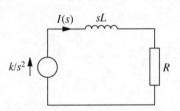

Fig. 4.8 Example

Thus

$$I(s) = \frac{k}{s^2(sL + R)} = \frac{(k/R)(R/L)}{s^2(s + R/L)}$$

This equation is of the form $a/[s^2(s + a)]$ with $a = R/L$, hence using item 11 in table 1.1 the inverse transform is

$$i = \frac{k}{R}\left[t - \frac{1 - e^{-Rt/L}}{R/L} \right]$$

$$= \frac{kt}{R} - \frac{kL}{R^2} + \frac{kL}{R^2} e^{-Rt/L}$$

Example

Derive an expression showing how the current in the circuit in figure 4.9 will vary with time when there is a 10 V step input to the circuit.

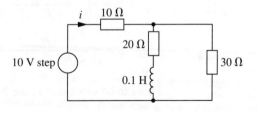

Fig. 4.9 Example

In the s-domain, the total circuit impedance $Z(s)$ is, using the equations for summing impedances in series and parallel,

$$Z(s) = 10 + \frac{30(20 + 0.1s)}{30 + 20 + 0.1s}$$

$$= \frac{1100 + 4s}{50 + 0.1s}$$

In the s-domain the step voltage is $10/s$. Thus

$$I(s) = \frac{10/s}{Z(s)} = \frac{500 + 1s}{s(1100 + 4s)}$$

$$= \frac{500}{s(1100 + 4s)} + \frac{1}{(1100 + 4s)}$$

$$= \frac{125}{s(s + 275)} + \frac{0.25}{(s + 275)}$$

Hence using items 8 and 7 in table 1.1

$$i = \tfrac{125}{275}(1 - e^{-275t}) + 0.25\,e^{-275t} \text{ A}$$

Example

Derive an equation showing how the current varies with time for a circuit consisting of resistance, inductance and capacitance in series when there is a step input voltage of v at the time $t = 0$.

In the s-domain the series arrangement has an impedance of

$$Z(s) = R + sL + \frac{1}{sC}$$

Hence, since the step voltage in the s-domain is v/s

$$I(s) = \frac{v/s}{Z(s)} = \frac{v}{s(R + sL + 1/sC)}$$

$$= \frac{v/L}{s^2 + (R/L)s + (1/LC)}$$

This can be expressed in the form

$$I(s) = \frac{v/L}{(s - p_1)(s - p_2)}$$

where p_1 and p_2 are the roots of the quadratic equation. Thus

$$p_1 = -\frac{R}{2L} + \sqrt{\left(\frac{R}{2L}\right)^2 - \frac{1}{LC}}$$

$$p_2 = -\frac{R}{2L} - \sqrt{\left(\frac{R}{2L}\right)^2 - \frac{1}{LC}}$$

When these roots are positive, i.e. $(R/2L)^2 > (1/LC)$, then the inverse transform can be obtained using item 12 in table 1.1 and so

$$i = \frac{v/L}{p_2 - p_1}(e^{-p_1 t} - e^{-p_2 t})$$

This is the overdamped condition.

When $(R/2L)^2 = (1/LC)$ then the two roots are equal with $p_1 = p_2 = -(R/2L)$. The denominator is then of the form $(s - a)^2$ and so the inverse transform can be obtained using item 9 in table 1.1. Thus

$$i = \frac{v}{L}t\, e^{-Rt/2L}$$

This is referred to as the critically damped response.

With $(R/2L)^2 < (1/LC)$ then the roots are complex numbers. One way we can tackle this is to manipulate the denominator into the form $(s + a)^2 + b^2$. This can be done by writing it as

$$s^2 + (R/L)s + (R/2L)^2 + (1/LC) - (R/2L)^2$$

$$= (s + R/2L)^2 + \left[(1/LC) - (R/2L)^2\right]$$

Hence we can write

$$I(s) = \frac{v/L}{\sqrt{(1/LC) - (R/2L)^2}}$$

$$\times \frac{\sqrt{(1/LC) - (R/2L)^2}}{(s + R/2L)^2 + \left[\sqrt{(1/LC) - (R/2L)^2}\right]^2}$$

Then using item 18 in table 1.1 gives

$$i = \frac{v/L}{\sqrt{(1/LC) - (R/2L)^2}}\, e^{-Rt/2L}\sin\left[(1/LC) - (R/2L)^2\right]t$$

The result is a damped oscillation. Such a condition is said to be underdamped.

Review problems

8   A 0.1 F capacitor that is uncharged at time $t = 0$ and a resistance of 5 Ω are in series with a voltage source of 20 V that is switched from zero to this steady value at $t = 0$. Determine how the current varies with time.

9   A 0.1 F capacitor that has been charged to 20 V is discharged through a resistance of 5 Ω. Determine how the current varies with time.

10   A sinusoidal voltage of $v \sin \omega t$ is applied at the time $t = 0$ to a circuit consisting of an inductance L in series with a resistance R. Determine how the current varies with time.

11   For the circuit shown in figure 4.10, determine how the current varies with time when the switch is closed.

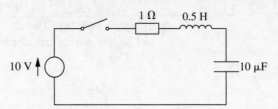

Fig. 4.10 Problem 11

12   A circuit consists of an uncharged capacitor C in series with a resistance R. Determine how the current varies with time when a ramp voltage of vt is applied.

13   A series circuit has a resistance of 12 Ω, an inductance of 2 H and an uncharged capacitance of 0.02 F. It is subject to a 4 V step voltage at time $t = 0$. Determine how the current varies with time.

4.2.4 Mesh and node analysis

The circuit analysis techniques of mesh and node analysis can be applied to networks in the s-domain. Thus, for example, for a network involving two meshes there will be two simultaneous equations that can be solved algebraically.

Example

Determine how the current through the 30 Ω resistor in figure 4.11 varies with time when the input is a step voltage of 10 V at time $t = 0$.

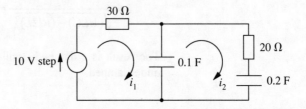

Fig. 4.11 Example

Using mesh analysis for the circuit in the *s*-domain, Kirchhoff's voltage law gives for each mesh

$$30I_1(s) + \frac{1}{0.1s}[I_1(s) - I_2(s)] = \frac{10}{s}$$

$$20I_2(s) + \frac{1}{0.2s}I_2(s) + \frac{1}{0.1s}[I_2(s) - I_1(s)] = 0$$

These can be simplified to give

$$\left[3 + \frac{1}{s}\right]I_1(s) - \frac{1}{s}I_2(s) = \frac{1}{s}$$

$$[3s + 1]I_1(s) - I_2(s) = 1$$

and

$$\left[4 + \frac{1}{s} + \frac{2}{s}\right]I_2(s) - \frac{2}{s}I_1(s) = 0$$

$$[4s + 3]I_2(s) - 2I_1(s) = 0$$

The two simultaneous equations can be solved to give $I_1(s)$. Thus

$$[3s + 1]I_1(s) - \frac{2I_1(s)}{4s + 3} = 1$$

Hence

$$I_1(s) = \frac{4s + 3}{12s^2 + 13s + 1}$$

$$= \frac{4s + 3}{(12s + 1)(s + 1)}$$

Expansion by means of partial fractions gives

$$I_1(s) = \frac{32}{11(12s + 1)} + \frac{1}{11(s + 1)}$$

Hence

$$i_1 = \frac{8}{33}e^{-t/12} + \frac{1}{11}e^{-t} \text{ A}$$

Review problems

14 Determine the current through the 30 Ω resistor for the circuit shown in figure 4.12 when it is subject to a 20 V step at time $t = 0$.

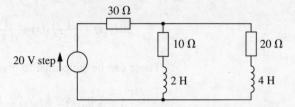

Fig. 4.12 Problem 14

15 Determine the current through the 1 Ω resistor for the circuit shown in figure 4.13 when it is subject to a 2 V impulse at time $t = 0$.

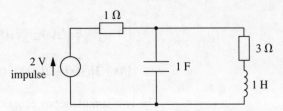

Fig. 4.13 Problem 15

Further problems

16 What are the impedances in the s-domain of (a) a 1 kΩ resistance, (b) a 0.5 H inductance, (c) a 2 μF capacitance?

17 What are the impedances in the s-domain of (a) a resistance of 100 Ω in series with an inductance of 10 mH, (b) a resistance of 1 kΩ in series with a capacitance of 10 μF, (c) a resistance of 1 kΩ, an inductance of 10 mH and a capacitance of 10 μF in series, (d) a resistance of 100 Ω in parallel with an inductance of 10 mH, (e) an inductance of 10 mH in parallel with a capacitance of 10 μF?

18 Determine how the current varies with time for a circuit consisting of a coil of resistance 20 Ω and inductance 1 H when it is suddenly connected to a voltage of 2 V.

19 Determine how, for the circuit in figure 4.14, the potential difference v varies with time when the switch is closed. The initial conditions are zero.

20 A circuit consists of a 1 MΩ resistor in series with a 0.1 μF capacitor. Determine how the voltage across the capacitor varies with time when there is a step voltage input of 6 V. The initial conditions are zero.

21 Determine how the current through the 75 Ω resistor will vary with time for the circuit shown in figure 4.15 when the switch is closed.

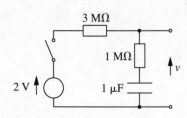

Fig. 4.14 Problem 19

Fig. 4.15 Problem 21

22 A coil of resistance R and inductance L is in parallel with a capacitance C. If the initial conditions are zero, derive a relationship for the current variation with time when a ramp input voltage of kt is applied to the combination. The initial conditions are zero.

23 A coil of resistance 1 Ω and inductance 0.5 H is in series with a capacitor of 2 mF. Derive a relationship showing how the current through the circuit will change with time when a voltage of 10 V is suddenly applied to the circuit. The initial conditions are zero.

24 A 1.25 kΩ resistor, a 0.25 H inductor and a 1 μF capacitor are connected in series. How does the potential difference across the capacitor vary with time when a step voltage of 30 V is applied to the circuit?

25 The switch in the circuit shown in figure 4.16 has been in position a for a long time. Derive an equation describing how the current through the resistor will vary with time when the switch is moved from a to b.

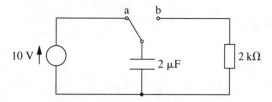

Fig. 4.16 Problem 25

26 Repeat problem 25 with the 2 kΩ resistor replaced by a 0.5 H inductor.

27 Determine how the current i varies with time when the switch is moved from position a to b, after being a long time at a, in the circuit described by figure 4.17.

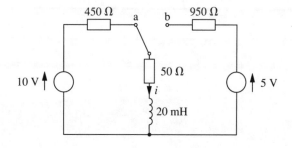

Fig. 4.17 Problem 27

28 Determine how the current varies with time when a sinusoidal voltage $10 \sin 10^6 t$ volts is applied to a circuit consisting of an initially uncharged 0.05 μF capacitor in series with a 50 Ω resistor.

29 Determine how the current i varies with time for the circuit described by figure 4.18 when a step voltage of 2 V is applied. All the initial conditions are zero.

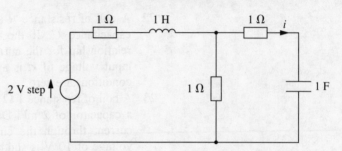

Fig. 4.18 Problem 29

30 Determine how the current i varies with time for the circuit shown in figure 4.19. All the initial conditions are zero.

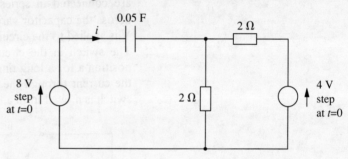

Fig. 4.19 Problem 30

5 System transfer functions

5.1 The transfer function

A useful and often used pictorial representation of a system is as a *block diagram*. Individual blocks are used to represent separate functional parts of the system. The contents of any one block is largely unimportant compared to its function. We might thus refer to a block as a *black box*. Thus, for example, we might have a system consisting of just an amplifier. The block diagram for this system can thus be just a single block with the function of amplification, i.e. giving a bigger output signal than the input signal. A music centre might consist of a number of interlinked blocks, e.g. a record player, a cassette deck, a radio, a function switching unit and an amplifier. Each of the blocks has a particular function, e.g. the record player converts the information stored in the grooves of a record into electrical signals.

In the case of a block like an amplifier it is customary to talk of the *gain* of the amplifier. This states how much bigger the output signal will be when compared with the input signal. It enables the output to be determined for specific inputs. Thus, for example, an amplifier with a voltage gain of 10 will give for an input voltage of 2 mV an output of 20 mV or if the input is 1 V an output of 10 V. The gain states the mathematical relationship between the output and the input for the block. However, for many blocks the relationship between the output and the input is in the form of a differential equation and so a statement of the function as just a simple number like the gain of 10 is not possible. For such blocks the function describing the relationship between output and input is in terms of what is termed the *transfer function*. The transfer function states the relationship between the Laplace transform of the output and the Laplace transform of the input. It enables the Laplace transform of the output from a block to be determined for different inputs.

Suppose that the input to a linear system has a Laplace transform of $X(s)$ and the Laplace transform of the output is $Y(s)$, with all the initial conditions being zero. The *transfer function* $G(s)$ of the system is then defined as

$$G(s) = \frac{Y(s)}{X(s)} \qquad [1]$$

This can be written as

$$Y(s) = G(s)X(s)$$

Thus the output transform is the product of the input transform and the transfer function. If we represent a system by a black box or block diagram (figure 5.1) then $G(s)$ is the function in the box which takes an input of $X(s)$ and converts it to an output of $Y(s)$. The system transfer function can be derived from the system differential equation by taking the Laplace transform of the equation and ignoring all terms arising from initial values.

A *linear system* is one for which if an input x_1 produces an output y_1 and an input x_2 gives an output y_2, then an input of $x_1 + x_2$ will give an output of $y_1 + y_2$.

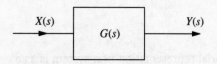

$X(s)$ $G(s)$ $Y(s)$

Fig. 5.1 Block diagram representation

5.1.1 First-order systems

Consider a block where the relationhsip between the input and the output is in the form of a first-order differential equation. The differential equation of a first-order system is of the form

$$a_1 \frac{dy}{dt} + a_0 y = b_0 x$$

where a_1, a_0, b_0 are constants and x is the input and y the output, both being functions of time. The Laplace transform of this, with all initial conditions zero, is

$$a_1 sY(s) + a_0 Y(s) = b_0 X(s)$$

and so

$$G(s) = \frac{Y(s)}{X(s)} = \frac{b_0}{a_1 s + a_0}$$

This can be rearranged to give

$$G(s) = \frac{b_0/a_0}{(a_1/a_0)s + 1} = \frac{G}{\tau s + 1} \qquad [2]$$

where G is the *gain* of the system when there are steady state conditions, i.e. there is no dy/dt term. (a_1/a_0) is the time constant τ of the system.

When a first-order system is subject to a unit step input then $X(s) = 1/s$ and the output transform $Y(s)$ is

$$Y(s) = G(s)X(s) = \frac{G}{s(\tau s + 1)}$$

$$= G\frac{(1/\tau)}{s(s + 1/\tau)}$$

Hence

$$y = G(1 - e^{-t/\tau})$$

Example

A circuit has a resistance R in series with capacitance C. The input to the circuit is v and the output is the potential difference v_C across the capacitor. What is the transfer function if the differential equation relating the input and output is

$$v = RC\frac{dv_C}{dt} + v_C$$

Taking the Laplace transform, with all initial conditions zero, then

$$V(s) = RCsV_C(s) + V_C(s)$$

Hence

$$G(s) = \frac{V_C(s)}{V(s)} = \frac{1}{RCs + 1}$$

Review problems

1 A hydraulic system has an input q and an output h related by the following differential equation. What is the transfer function for the system?

$$q = A\frac{dh}{dt} + \frac{\rho gh}{R}$$

2 In general a first-order system can be described by equation [2]. How does the output of such a system vary with time when it is subject to (a) a unit ramp input, (b) a unit impulse input?

3   A thermocouple has a transfer function linking its voltage output and temperature input of

$$G(s) = \frac{30 \times 10^{-6}}{10s + 1} \text{ V/}°\text{C}$$

(a) What will be the time taken for the output to reach 95% of its final value when it is subject to a step input of 100 °C?
(b) What will be the output after 12 s when the thermocouple is subject to a steadily rising input of 5 °C/s?
(c) What will be the output 5 s after the thermocouple has been subject to a temperature impulse of 100 °C?

5.1.2 Second-order systems

For a second-order system, the relationship between the input $X(s)$ and the output $Y(s)$ is described by a differential equation of the form

$$a_2 \frac{d^2 y}{dt^2} + a_1 \frac{dy}{dt} + a_0 y = b_0 x$$

where a_2, a_1, a_0 and b_0 are constants. The Laplace transform of this equation, with all initial conditions zero, is

$$a_2 s^2 Y(s) + a_1 s Y(s) + a_0 Y(s) = b_0 X(s)$$

Hence

$$G(s) = \frac{Y(s)}{X(s)} = \frac{b_0}{a_2 s^2 + a_1 s + a_0} \qquad [3]$$

An alternative way of writing the differential equation for a second-order system is

$$\frac{d^2 y}{dt^2} + 2\zeta\omega_n \frac{dy}{dt} + \omega_n^2 y = b_0 \omega_n^2 x$$

where ω_n is the natural angular frequency with which the system oscillates and ζ is the damping ratio. The Laplace transform of this equation gives

$$G(s) = \frac{Y(s)}{X(s)} = \frac{b_0 \omega_n^2}{s^2 + 2\zeta\omega_n s + \omega_n^2} \qquad [4]$$

Equation [3] or [4] is the general form taken by the transfer function for a second-order system.

When a second-order system is subject to a unit step input, i.e. $X(s) = 1/s$, then the output transform is

$$Y(s) = \frac{b_0 \omega_n^2}{s(s^2 + 2\zeta\omega_n s + \omega_n)}$$

This can be rearranged as

$$Y(s) = \frac{b_0 \omega_n^2}{s(s + p_1)(s + p_2)} \qquad [5]$$

where p_1 and p_2 are the roots of the equation

$$s^2 + 2\zeta\omega_n s + \omega_n = 0$$

Hence

$$p = \frac{-2\zeta\omega_n \pm \sqrt{4\zeta^2\omega_n^2 - 4\omega_n^2}}{2}$$

and so

$$p_1 = -\zeta\omega_n + \omega_n\sqrt{\zeta^2 - 1} \qquad [6]$$

$$p_2 = -\zeta\omega_n - \omega_n\sqrt{\zeta^2 - 1} \qquad [7]$$

With $\zeta > 1$ the square root term is real and the system is said to be overdamped. The inverse transform of equation [5] is then given by item 14 in table 1.1 as

$$y = \frac{b_0 \omega_n^2}{p_1 p_2}\left[1 - \frac{p_2}{p_2 - p_1} e^{-p_2 t} + \frac{p_1}{p_2 - p_1} e^{-p_1 t} \right] \qquad [8]$$

With $\zeta = 1$ the square root term in equations [6] and [7] is zero and so $p_1 = p_2 = -\omega_n$. Equation [5] then becomes

$$Y(s) = \frac{b_0 \omega_n^2}{s(s + \omega_n)^2}$$

This equation can be expanded by means of partial fractions to give

$$Y(s) = b_0 \omega_n^2\left[\frac{1}{s} - \frac{1}{s + \omega_n} - \frac{\omega_n}{(s + \omega_n)^2} \right]$$

Hence

$$y = b_0\omega_n^2[1 - e^{-\omega_n t} - \omega_n t e^{-\omega_n t}] \tag{9}$$

With $\zeta < 1$ then equation [5] gives the inverse transform, using item 28 in table 1.1,

$$y = b_0\left[1 - \frac{e^{-\zeta\omega_n t}}{\sqrt{1-\zeta^2}} \sin\left(\omega_n \sqrt{(1-\zeta^2)}\, t + \phi\right)\right] \tag{10}$$

where $\cos\phi = \zeta$. This is an underdamped oscillation.

Example

What is the state of damping of a system having the following transfer function and subject to a unit step input?

$$G(s) = \frac{1}{s^2 + 8s + 16}$$

For a unit step input $X(s) = 1/s$ and so the output transform is

$$Y(s) = \frac{1}{s(s^2 + 8s + 16)}$$

This can be simplified to

$$Y(s) = \frac{1}{s(s+4)(s+4)}$$

The roots of $s^2 + 8s + 16$ are thus $p_1 = p_2 = -4$. Both the roots are real and the same and so the system is critically damped.

Revision problems

4   What is the transfer function for a system with input x and output y related by the following differential equation?

$$\frac{d^2y}{dx^2} + 4\frac{dy}{dx} + 5y = 3x$$

5   What is the state of the damping of a second-order system which has a damping factor of 0.4 and a natural angular frequency of 10 rad/s and subject to a unit step input?

6   Derive the equation describing how the output of the system in problem 5 will change with time.

7   A robot arm having the following transfer function is subject to a unit ramp input. Derive an equation showing how the output varies with time.

$$G(s) = \frac{K}{(s+3)^2}$$

8   How does the output vary with time for a system having the following transfer function when it is subject to an input of $6e^{-2t}$?

$$G(s) = \frac{s}{s^2 + 4s + 3}$$

5.2 Systems in series

If a system consists of a number of sub-systems in series, as in figure 5.2, then the transfer function $G(s)$ of the system is given by

$$G(s) = \frac{Y(s)}{X(s)}$$

$$= \frac{Y_1(s)}{X(s)} \times \frac{Y_2(s)}{Y_1(s)} \times \frac{Y(s)}{Y_2(s)}$$

$$= G_1(s) \times G_2(s) \times G_3(s) \qquad [11]$$

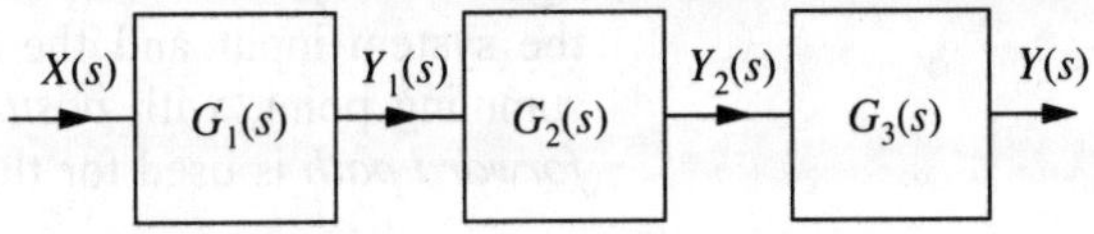

Fig. 5.2 Systems in series

It has been assumed that when the sub-systems were linked together that no interaction occurs between the blocks which would result in changes in the transfer functions. Thus if the sub-systems are electrical circuits there can be problems when the circuits interact and load each other.

Example

What is the overall transfer function for a system consisting of three elements in series, the transfer functions of the elements being 10, $2/s$, and $4/(s + 3)$?

Using equation [11],

$$G(s) = 10 \times \frac{2}{s} \times \frac{4}{s+3} = \frac{80}{s(s+3)}$$

Review problems

9   A field-controlled d.c. motor consists of three sub-systems in series, the field circuit, the armature coil and the load. Figure 5.3 illustrates the arrangement and the transfer functions of the sub-systems. What is the transfer function of the motor?

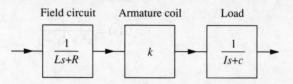

Field circuit   Armature coil   Load

Fig. 5.3 Problem 9

10   A system consists of two sub-systems in series and having the following transfer functions. What is the overall transfer function of the system?

$$\frac{2}{s+1} \text{ and } \frac{1}{s-1}$$

5.3 Systems with feedback loops

Figure 5.4(a) shows a simple system having negative feedback, figure 5.4(b) one with positive feedback. With *negative feedback* the system input and the feedback signals are subtracted at the summing point, with *positive feedback* they are added. The term *forward path* is used for the path having the transfer function $G(s)$

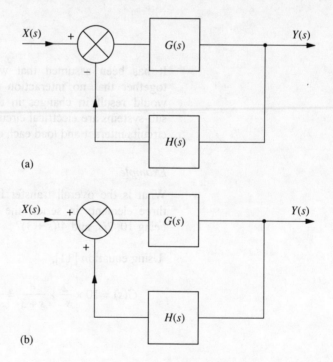

(a)

(b)

Fig. 5.4 (a) Negative feedback, (b) positive feedback

in the figure and *feedback path* for the one having $H(s)$. The entire system is referred to as a *closed loop system*.

For the negative feedback system, the input to the sub-system having the transfer function $G(s)$ is $X(s)$ minus the feedback signal. The feedback loop has a transfer function of $H(s)$ and thus the feedback signal is $H(s)Y(s)$. Since the output from the $G(s)$ element is $Y(s)$ then

$$G(s) = \frac{Y(s)}{X(s) - H(s)Y(s)}$$

This can be rearranged to give

$$[1 + G(s)H(s)]Y(s) = G(s)X(s)$$

Hence the overall transfer function $T(s)$ is

$$T(s) = \frac{Y(s)}{X(s)} = \frac{G(s)}{1 + G(s)H(s)} \qquad [12]$$

If the feedback is positive the overall transfer function becomes

$$T(s) = \frac{G(s)}{1 - G(s)H(s)} \qquad [13]$$

Example

What is the overall transfer function for a closed loop system having a forward path transfer function of $2/(s + 1)$ and a negative feedback path transfer function of $5s$?

Using equation [12],

$$T(s) = \frac{G(s)}{1 + G(s)H(s)} = \frac{2/(s + 1)}{1 + [2/(s + 1)]5s}$$

$$= \frac{2}{11s + 1}$$

Review problems

11 What is the overall transfer function for a closed loop system having a forward path transfer function of $5/(s + 3)$ and a negative feedback path transfer function of 10?

12 A closed loop system has a forward path having two series elements with transfer functions 5 and $1/(s + 1)$. If the feedback path has a transfer function $2/s$, what is the overall transfer function of the system?

13 A closed loop system has a forward path having two series elements with transfer functions of 2 and $1/(s + 1)$. If the feedback path has a transfer function of s, what is the overall transfer function of the system?

14 What would be the overall transfer function of the system described in problem 13 if the feedback had been positive?

15 An armature-controlled d.c. motor has a forward path consisting of three elements, the armature circuit with a transfer function $1/(Ls + R)$, the armature coil with a transfer function k and the load with a transfer function $1/(Is + c)$. There is a negative feedback path with a transfer function K. What is the overall transfer function of the motor?

16 A position control system has a negative feedback path with a transfer function of 1 and two sub-systems in its forward path, a controller with a transfer function of K and a motor/drive system with a transfer function of

$$\frac{1}{s(s+1)}$$

What value of K is necessary for the system to be critically damped?

5.4 Poles and zeros

In section 5.1.2 a second-order system was considered. In order to see how the output, for a particular input, would vary with time the denominator of the transfer function equation was put into the form $(s+p_1)(s+p_2)$, (see for example equation [5]). The form of the output from the system depended very much on the values of these roots p_1 and p_2. With real values for the roots the system gave an overdamped response to a unit step input, with the roots containing an imaginary term then the system gave an oscillatory response.

In general, the transfer function for a system can be written in the form

$$G(s) = \frac{K(s-z_1)(s-z_2)...(s-z_m)}{(s-p_1)(s-p_2)...(s-p_n)} \qquad [14]$$

where $z_1, z_2, ... z_m$ are the values of s that make the numerator of the transfer function zero. They are known as the *zeros* and are the roots of the numerator. $p_1, p_2, ... p_n$ are the values of s that make the denominator zero and hence the transfer function infinite. They are known as the *poles* and are the roots of the denominator. K is a constant. Zeros and poles can be real or complex quantities.

Example

What are the zeros and poles of the systems having the following transfer functions?

(a) $G(s) = \dfrac{s-5}{s^2 - 4s + 4}$, (b) $G(s) = \dfrac{s+2}{s^2 + 2s + 3}$,

(c) $G(s) = \dfrac{4}{s(s-5)}$

(a) The numerator is $(s-5)$ and so there is a zero of $s = +5$. The denominator can be written as $(s-2)(s-2)$ and so there are poles of $s = +2$ and $s = +2$.

(b) The numerator is $(s+2)$ and so there is a zero of $s = -2$. The roots of the denominator can be obtained by using the equation for the roots of a quadratic equation. They are thus given by

$$s = \frac{-1 \pm \sqrt{1 - 12}}{2} = \frac{-1 \pm \sqrt{-1}\sqrt{12 - 1}}{2}$$

$$= -0.5 \pm j1.7$$

Hence the poles are $s = -0.5 + j1.7$ and $s = -0.5 - j1.7$.

(c) There are no zeros. The poles are $s = 0$ and $s = +5$.

Review problems

17 What are the zeros and poles of the systems giving the following transfer functions?

(a) $G(s) = \dfrac{2(s+4)}{(s+1)(s+2)}$, (b) $G(s) = \dfrac{5}{s(s+1)}$,

(c) $G(s) = \dfrac{s+3}{s^2 - 2s + 5}$, (d) $G(s) = \dfrac{3s}{s^2 + 4s + 5}$

5.4.1 Stability

Think of a ball resting in a saucer. If the ball is given an impulse, i.e. a push, then it moves out from the centre of the saucer but then oscillates back and forth in the saucer until eventually it comes to rest. The system is said to be *stable*. If the ball was however resting on an upturned saucer then the effect of the impulse would be to move the ball out from the centre and it would then keep on moving and not return back to the centre. The system is said to be *unstable*. If the ball was resting on a horizontal surface then the impulse would just push the ball from one stable position to a new stable position somewhere else along the surface. Such a system is said to be *critically* or *marginally stable*.

If a system is stable then when it has an input of an impulse the output decays with time. With an unstable system the output increases with time after such an input. With a critically stable system the output tends to a new constant value after an impulse input.

Equation [14] can be written, by the use of partial fractions, in the form

$$G(s) = \frac{A}{s+p_1} + \frac{B}{s+p_2} + \frac{C}{s+p_3} + \dots$$

The poles in the above expression all have negative values. Then, for a unit impulse input, the inverse transform gives

$$y = A\,e^{-p_1 t} + B\,e^{-p_2 t} + C\,e^{-p_3 t} + \dots$$

The output contains only exponential terms with negative indices, i.e. of the form e^{-at}, and so decays to zero with time. With such terms then the denominator of the transfer function only contains terms of the form $(s+a)$, i.e. s has only negative values. If one of the poles has a positive value, i.e. the transfer function denominator contains a term of the form $(s-a)$, then the output, with an impulse input, will contain a term of the form e^{at}. This increases with time and so the system is unstable. Roots can be real or complex quantities. For stability all the poles should have real parts which are negative. For instability there needs to be just one pole which has a real part which is positive. A system is said to be critically stable if there is a root of $s = 0$ and all the other roots have negative values. The output from such a system, when subject to an impulse input, will contain a time independent term. Thus for example, the transfer function $a/[s(s + a)]$ has the inverse transform of $1 - e^{-at}$.

1   It is necessary for the real part of a particular pole to be negative if the transient resulting from that pole is to decay with time. If it is positive the transient response will increase with time and the system is unstable.
2   The more negative the real part of a pole the faster its transient decays with time.
3   Poles with imaginary components occur in pairs, $a \pm jb$, and the transient resulting from this pair has the form of a sinusoidal term multiplied by an exponential term. For stability the real part should be negative.

Figure 5.5 shows how, for a number of simple systems, the output depends on the pole values. The pole values have been

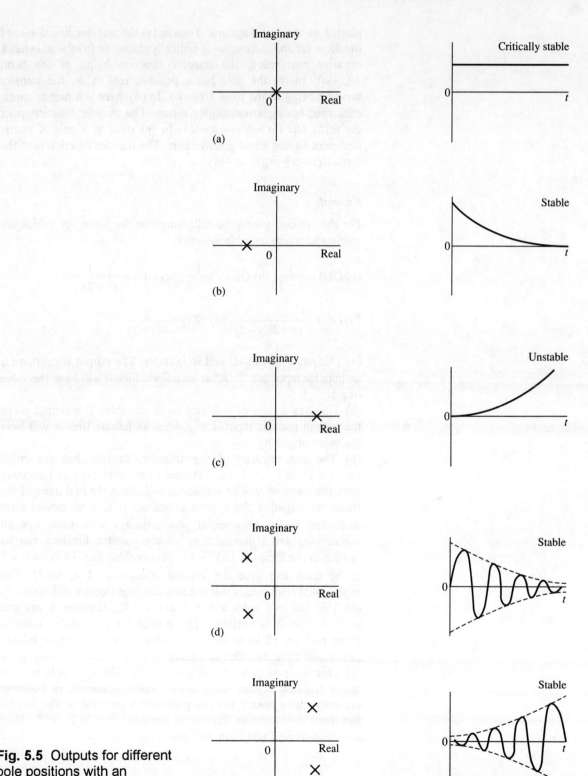

Fig. 5.5 Outputs for different pole positions with an impulse input

plotted on Argand diagrams. Thus in (a) the transfer function is of the form $1/s$ and the output is critically stable. In (b) the pole has a negative real value, the transfer function being of the form $1/(s+a)$. In (c) the pole has a positive real value, the transfer function being of the form $1/(s-a)$. In (d) there is a pair of roots, each root having a real negative part. The transfer function is of the form $1/(s+a+jb)(s+a-jb)$. In (e) there is a pair of roots, each root having a real positive part. The transfer function is of the form $1/(s-a+jb)(s-a-jb)$.

Example

For the systems giving the following transfer functions, which are stable and which unstable systems?

(a) $G(s) = \dfrac{1}{s+2}$, (b) $G(s) = \dfrac{1}{s-2}$, (c) $G(s) = \dfrac{1}{s^2+2s+5}$,

(d) $G(s) = \dfrac{1}{(s+2)(s-2)}$, (e) $G(s) = \dfrac{2}{s(s+2)}$

(a) This has a pole of -2 and so is stable. The output when there is an impulse input is e^{-2t}. After an infinite time it will have the value of zero.

(b) This has a pole of $+2$ and so is unstable. The output when there is an impulse input is e^{2t}. After an infinite time it will have the value of infinity.

(c) The denominator of the transfer function has the roots $s = -1 + j2$ and $s = -1 - j2$. Because the roots have an imaginary term the transient will be sinusoidal and since the real parts of the roots are negative the system is stable. It is a sinusoidal term multiplied by an exponential which decays with time. For an impulse input the denominator of the transfer function can be written in the form $\left[(s+1)^2 + 4 \right]$. This enables item 18 in table 1.1 to be used and give the inverse transform of $e^{-t} \sin 2t$. The exponential term means that the sine function decays with time.

(d) This has two poles $s = +2$ and $s = -2$. Because it has one positive pole it is unstable. The output for an impulse input is given by item 12 in table 1.1 as $-4(e^{-2t} - e^{2t})$. After an infinite time it will have the value of infinity.

(e) This has two poles $s = 0$ and $s = -2$. The system is not unstable because it has no positive value poles. It is however critically stable since it has one pole with a zero value. The inverse transform of this, when there is an impulse input, is $1 - e^{-2t}$. After an infinite time it will have the value 1.

Example

A circuit has a resistance R in series with capacitance C. The input to the circuit is v_C across the capacitor. Is the system stable?

The transfer function of such a system (see the example in section 5.1.1) is given by

$$G(s) = \frac{1}{RCs+1} = \frac{(1/RC)}{(s+1/RC)}$$

The denominator thus has the root of $-1/RC$ and thus, since both R and C will be real and positive quantities, the system is stable.

Review problems

18 For the systems giving the following transfer functions, which are stable and which unstable?

(a) $G(s) = \dfrac{1}{s-5}$, (b) $G(s) = \dfrac{1}{s+3}$, (c) $G(s) = \dfrac{1}{s^2+4s+3}$,

(d) $G(s) = \dfrac{1}{s^2+3s-10}$, (e) $G(s) = \dfrac{1}{s^2-2s+10}$,

(f) $G(s) = \dfrac{1}{s(s+1)(s+2)}$, (g) $G(s) = \dfrac{1}{(s^2+1)(s+2)}$

Further problems

19 What are the transfer functions for systems giving the following input/output relationships?
(a) An RC circuit with an input v and output i, where

$$v = Ri + \frac{1}{C}\int i\, dt$$

(b) A spring–dashpot–mass system with an input F and an output x, where

$$m\frac{d^2x}{dt^2} + c\frac{dx}{dt} + kx = F$$

(c) An RLC circuit with an input v and output v_C, where

$$v = RC\frac{dv_C}{dt} + LC\frac{d^2v_C}{dt^2} + v_C$$

20 Determine the transfer functions for the electrical circuits shown in figure 5.6.

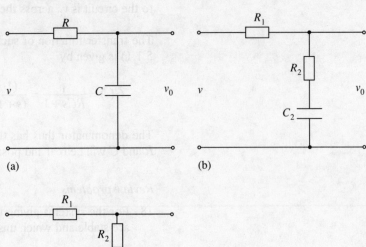

(a)

(b)

Fig. 5.6 Problem 20   (c)

21 What are the time constants of the systems giving the following transfer functions?

(a) $G(s) = \dfrac{5}{3s+1}$, (b) $G(s) = \dfrac{3}{2s+3}$

22 Determine how the outputs of the following systems vary with time when subject to a unit step input at time $t = 0$.

(a) $G(s) = \dfrac{2}{s+2}$, (b) $G(s) = \dfrac{10}{s+5}$

23 What is the state of the damping for the systems having the following transfer functions?

(a) $G(s) = \dfrac{5}{s^2 - 6s + 16}$, (b) $G(s) = \dfrac{10}{s^2 + s + 100}$,

(c) $G(s) = \dfrac{2s+1}{s^2 + 2s + 1}$, (d) $G(s) = \dfrac{3s+20}{s^2 + 2s + 20}$

24 What is the output of a system with the following transfer function and subject to a unit step input at time $t = 0$?

$$G(s) = \frac{s}{(s+3)^2}$$

25 What is the output of a system having the following transfer function and subject to a unit impulse?

$$G(s) = \frac{2}{(s+3)(s+4)}$$

26 What is the damping ratio and the natural angular frequency of the system having the following transfer function?

$$G(s) = \frac{s+10}{s^2 + 2s + 25}$$

27 What value of the constant K is required for the system with the following transfer function to give an output with a damping ratio of 0.6?

$$G(s) = \frac{12}{s^2 + 12s + K}$$

28 The side-to-side oscillations of a ship due to waves, i.e. the rolling motion, can be described by

$$\frac{\Theta(s)}{H(s)} = \frac{\omega_n^2}{s^2 + 2\zeta\omega_n s + \omega_n^2}$$

where θ is the angular deflection from the vertical and h the height of the waves. With the natural angular frequency ω_n as 2 rad/s and the damping factor ζ as 0.1, how does the angular deflection vary with time when the ship is subject to a sudden large wave, i.e. an impulse?

29 What are the overall transfer functions of the following negative feedback systems?

(a) Forward path $G(s) = \dfrac{4}{s(s+1)}$, feedback path $H(s) = \dfrac{1}{s}$;

(b) Forward path $G(s) = \dfrac{2}{s+1}$, feedback path $H(s) = \dfrac{1}{s+2}$;

(c) Forward path $G(s) = \dfrac{4}{(s+2)(s+3)}$, feedback path $H(s) = 5$;

(d) Forward path with two elements in series $G_1(s) = \dfrac{2}{s+2}$

and $G_2(s) = \dfrac{1}{s}$, feedback path $H(s) = 10$.

30 A negative feedback system has a forward path with two elements, one having a constant value transfer function of K and the other a transfer function of $1/(s^2 + 10s + 2)$. If the feedback loop has a transfer function of 1, what is the value of K required for the system to have a damping factor of 0.7?

31 What are the poles and zeros of the systems giving the following transfer functions?

(a) $\dfrac{s-1}{s^2 - 5s + 6}$, (b) $\dfrac{s(s+1)}{(s+1)(s-1)(s-2)}$, (c) $\dfrac{2s-1}{s^2 + 2s}$,

(d) $\dfrac{5}{s^2 + 2s + 3}$

32 The following are the transfer functions of systems; which are stable, which critically stable and which unstable?

(a) $\dfrac{10}{s(s+1)}$, (b) $\dfrac{2}{(s-1)(s-2)}$, (c) $\dfrac{2s+1}{(s+2)(s+1)}$,

(d) $\dfrac{2}{s^2 + 8s + 8}$, (e) $\dfrac{2(s+1)}{s^2 + s + 5}$

33 A negative feedback system has a feedback loop with a transfer function of 1 and a forward transfer function of

$$\dfrac{2K}{(s+1)(s+2)}$$

For what value of K will the system have a damping factor of 0.7?

34 A negative feedback system has a feedback loop with a transfer function of 1 and a forward transfer function of

$$\dfrac{K}{s(s+1)}$$

For what value of K will the system be critically stable?

35 A circuit consists of an inductance L in series with an arrangement of a capacitance C in parallel with a resistance R. Derive the transfer function relating the input voltage to the output voltage across the capacitance. Hence determine the poles and whether the circuit is stable when $1/LC = 3$ $H^{-1}F^{-1}$ and $1/RC = 4$ $\Omega^{-1}F^{-1}$.

36 An field-controlled d.c. motor can be considered to consist of three series linked blocks, a field circuit with a transfer function of $1/(Ls + R)$, an armature coil with a transfer function of k and a load with a transfer function of $1/(Is + c)$. Determine the poles of the transfer function.

6 Sampled data systems and z-transforms

6.1 Sampled data systems

A digital thermometer is a device which gives a digital output for an analogue input, the temperature being an analogue quantity which varies continuously with time. A digital computer used as a controller in a feedback control system requires an input of signals in digital form. However the plant being controlled will generally be providing signals that vary continuously with time, i.e. they are analogue signals. With both these examples, the input signals have to be converted from analogue to digital form. Such a conversion requires the signal to be sampled at intervals, each sample then being converted into digital form. They can thus be described as *sampled data systems*.

To illustrate this, consider measurements made with a digital thermometer. The temperature varies continuously with time and this signal is sampled, say once every second. The value of the temperature at a sampling point is converted into a digital output. Thus once every second the temperature is sampled and the reading converted to digital form and hence displayed.

To indicate which signals are continuously varying with time and which are sampled, a starred symbol is generally used for sampled signals. Thus the analogue signal is represented by $f(t)$, this notation indicating it is a continuous function of time. When the signal has been sampled and converted to digital form the symbol becomes $f^*(t)$.

6.1.1 The sampling process

Consider a continuous input function $f(t)$. Samples of the input waveform are taken every T seconds. The sampling element senses the value of the signal over a short interval of time Δt in each sampling period and ignores it for the rest of the period. It can thus be considered to be a switch which is switched on every T seconds for just Δt. Figure 6.1 illustrates this sampling process for a continuous-time signal $f(t)$. Δt is small enough for each sampled

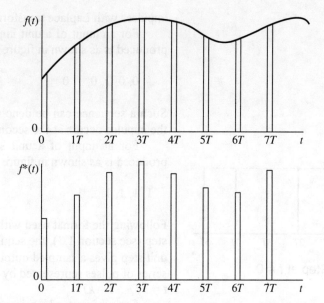

Fig. 6.1 The sampling process

signal to be considered of constant size during that time. The output is thus a series of pulses at regular time intervals, the height of a pulse at 0, $1T$, $2T$, $3T$, $4T$, ... kT, being a measure of the size of the continuous-time signal $f(t)$ at that time. We can represent the series of pulses up to some time kT as the number sequence

$$f(0), f(1T), f(2T), f(3T), ... f(kT)$$

where k is an integer and $f(0)$ is the value of the function at $t = 0$, $f(1T)$ is the value at $t = 1T$, etc.

We can denote the above sequence as being the function $f(kT)$, with k being the sample number. It is however quite common practice to denote such a sequence by just $f(k)$, with the fact that the sequence has been obtained by sampling being understood. Thus the above sequence would then be written as

$$f(0), f(1), f(2), f(3) ... f(k)$$

This notation is particularly appropriate if we are just concerned with a sequence of pulses and not what analogue signal they were obtained from.

Consider an analogue signal input which is just a unit impulse at $t = 0$. The sampled output is represented by figure 6.2(a), i.e. just a single pulse at $t = 0$. The series of pulses at the sampling times is thus

$$1, 0, 0, 0 ... 0$$

Such a sequence can be denoted, using the notation introduced for

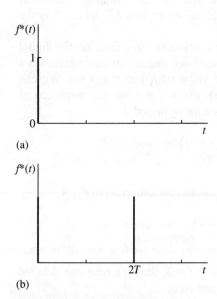

(a)

(b)

Fig. 6.2 Unit impulses at (a) $t = 0$, (b) $t = 2T$

impulses with Laplace transforms (section 1.4), by $\delta(k)$.

For an input of a unit impulse at $t = 2T$, the series of pulses produced is as shown in figure 6.2(b), i.e.

0, 0, 1, 0, ... 0

Such a sequence can be denoted by $\delta(k-2)$, the 2 indicating that the impulse occurs at the second sampling time.

For an input of a unit step at $t = 0$, the series of pulses produced is as shown in figure 6.3, i.e.

1, 1, 1, 1, ... 1

Following the format used with the Laplace transform for a unit step (see section 1.3), the sequence can be denoted by $u(k)$. The unit step gives a sampled output which is the same as the sum of a series of pulses represented by unit impulses at $t = 0$, $t = 1T$, $t = 2t$, $t = 3T$, ... $t = kT$.

For an input which is a ramp, starting at $t = 0$ and with a slope which increases by 1 for each sampling period, then the series of pulses produced is as shown in figure 6.4, i.e.

0, 1, 2, 3, ... k

The ramp gives a sampled output which is the same as the sum of a series of pulses produced by impulses of size 0 at $t = 0$, size 1 at $t = 1T$, size 2 at $t = 2T$, size 3 at $t = 3T$, ... size k at $t = kT$.

If we had the ramp signal $f(t) = t$ then sampling at intervals of T would give a sequence of pulses of size kT, where k is the sample number.

Whatever the form of the continuous-time function the digital output is a sequence of impulses. Each impulse in the sequence is a unit impulse multiplied by the value of $f(t)$ at that time. We can thus write for a function $f^*(t)$ which describes the sequence of pulses for a function $f(t)$ with sampling period T

$$f^*(t) = f(0)(\text{impulse at } 0) + f(1T)(\text{impulse at } 1T)$$
$$+ f(2T)(\text{impulse at } 2T) + ... + f(kT)(\text{impulse at } kT) \quad [1]$$

or using the notion for an impulse introduced in section 1.4,

$$f^*(t) = f(0)\delta(t) + f(1T)\delta(t - T)$$
$$+ f(2T)\delta(t - 2T) + ... + f(kT)\delta(t - kT)$$

Thus we have the first impulse at $t = 0$, then the next one delayed by T, then one delayed by $2T$, and so on.

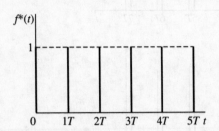

Fig. 6.3 Step at $t = 0$

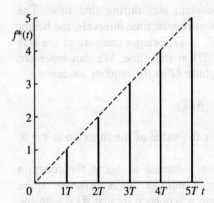

Fig. 6.4 Ramp starting at $t = 0$

Example

What is the sampled output from an analogue input of $f(t) = 2t$ when there is a sampling period of 1 s?

With $t = 0$ then $f(0) = 0$. With $t = 1T$ then $f(1T) = 2T = 2$. With $t = 2T$ then $f(2T) = 4T = 4$. With $t = 3T$ then $f(3T) = 6T = 6$. The sampled output is thus the series of impulses

0, 2, 4, 6, ...

Example

What is the sequence of pulses from a system with $f(k) = 2k$?

With $k = 0$ then the pulse has a size of 0, with $k = 1$ the pulse size is 2, with $k = 2$ it is 4, with $k = 3$ it is 6. The sequence is thus

0, 2, 4, 6, ...

Note that the sampled function which could give such a sequence is the ramp function $f(t) = 2t$. Different sample times would merely give different scaling factors for the above sequence. For example, with $T = 1$ s we would have

0, 2, 4, 6, ...

while with $T = 0.5$ s we would have

0, 1, 2, 3, ...

Review problems

1   What is the sampled output from the following analogue input s when there is a sampling period of 1 s?
(a) $f(t) = 2^t$, (b) $f(t) = 1 + 2t$, (c) $f(t) = e^{-t}$

2   What is the pulse sequence given by $f(k) = 0$ for $k = 0$, 1 and 2 and $f(k) = 1$ for $k = 3, 4, 5, ...$?

3   What expression for $f(k)$ would represent the samples taken with a sampling period of 0.1 s from the analogue signal $f(t) = e^{-0.5t}u(t)$?

6.2 The z-transform

The Laplace transform of an impulse at $t = 0$ is 1. The Laplace transform of an impulse at time T is e^{-Ts}, at time $2T$ it is e^{-2Ts}, and time kT is e^{-kTs}. Thus the Laplace transform of $f^*(t)$, i.e. equation [1], is

$$F^*(s) = f(0)1 + f(T)e^{-Ts} + f(2T)e^{-2Ts} + ... + f(kT)e^{-kTs} \qquad [2]$$

We can represent this as

$$F^*(s) = \sum_{k=0}^{k=\infty} f(kT)e^{-kTs} \qquad [3]$$

This can be simplified if we let

$$z = e^{Ts} \qquad [4]$$

This can also be written as

$$s = \frac{1}{T}\ln z \qquad [5]$$

$F^*(s)$, with s having the value given by equation [5], is called the *z-transform* of $f^*(t)$. This can be written as

$$\mathcal{Z}\{f^*(t)\} = F(z)$$

Since $f^*(t)$ is a sequence of pulses which can be represented by $f(k)$, then the above expression is often written as

$$\mathcal{Z}\{f(k)\} = F(z)$$

Equation [3] can thus be written as

$$F(z) = \sum_{k=0}^{k=\infty} f(kT)z^{-k} \qquad [6]$$

This, written out as the sequence of impulse terms, i.e. replacing e^{-Ts} terms in equation [2] by z terms, is

$$F(z) = f(0)z^0 + f(T)z^{-1} + f(2T)z^{-2} + ... + f(kT)z^{-k} \qquad [7]$$

Consider the z-transform for a unit step. Such a step has $f(t) = 1$ for all values of $t > 0$. Thus, using equation [7]

$$F(z) = 1z^0 + 1z^{-1} + 1z^{-2} + ... + 1z^{-k}$$

For a series of this form, a geometric series, we have the basic relationship

$$1 + x + x^2 + x^3 + ... = \frac{1}{1-x}$$

and thus if $x = 1/z$ then the sum of all these terms in z is

$$F(z) = \frac{1}{1 - 1/z} = \frac{z}{z - 1} \qquad [8]$$

This is a more convenient expression to handle than the series of terms for $f^*(t)$ or $F^*(s)$ for the unit step.

In general, if any continuous function has a Laplace transform then the corresponding sampled function has a z-transform.

Example

Determine the z-transform of a ramp function $f(t) = t$, as in figure 6.4. Sampling gives $f(t)$ with the values 0 at $t = 0$, $1T$ at $t = 1T$, $2T$ at $t = 2T$, $3T$ at $t = 3T$, etc.

Equation [7] gives

$$F(z) = 0 + Tz^{-1} + 2Tz^{-2} + 3Tz^{-3} + \ldots$$

This can be written as

$$\frac{zF(z)}{T} = 1 + 2z^{-1} + 3z^{-2} + \ldots$$

This is a series of the form

$$1 + 2x + 3x + \ldots = \frac{1}{(1-x)^2}$$

Thus with $x = 1/z$,

$$\frac{zF(z)}{T} = \frac{1}{(1 - 1/z)^2}$$

and so

$$F(z) = \frac{Tz}{(z-1)^2} \qquad [9]$$

Review problems

For the following problems, use the defining equation [7].

4   Determine the z-transforms of the sampled functions:
(a) $f(t) = e^{-at}$ when a is a constant, (b) $f(t) = 2^t$,
(c) $f(t) = 3t$, (d) $f(t) = 10$, (e) $10 + 3t$.

5   Determine the z-transforms of the following sequences:
(a) $f(0) = 0, f(1) = 0, f(2) = 1, f(3) = 1, ... f(k) = 1$;
(b) $f(0) = 0, f(1) = 3, f(2) = 6, f(3) = 9, ... f(k) = 3k$.

6.3 Standard z-transforms

In tackling problems requiring z-transforms to be obtained, it is not usually necessary to work from first principles since standard tables exist of the most commonly encountered z-transforms. Table 6.1 shows some of these. These transforms, when used with the z-transform properties outlined in the next section, enable a wide range of problems to be tackled.

Example

Determine, using table 6.1, the z-transforms for a sampling period of 1 s of the samples taken of (a) $f(t) = e^{-2t}$, (b) $f(t) = (1 - 3t)e^{-3t}$, (c) $f(t) = \sin 4t$.

(a) Using item 6 in the table,

$$Z\{f^*(t)\} = \frac{z}{z - e^{-2}}$$

(b) Using item 9 in the table

$$Z\{f^*(t)\} = \frac{z(1 - e^{-3})}{(z - 1)(z - e^{-3})}$$

(c) Using item 13 in the table

$$Z\{f^*(t)\} = \frac{z \sin 4}{z^2 - 2z \cos 4 + 1}$$

Example

Determine the z-transform of $e^{2k} \cos 3k$.

Item 16 in table 6.1 gives the z-transform for $e^{-akT} \cos k\omega T$. Thus if we take a to be -2, T to be 1 and ω to be 3, then

$$Z\{e^{2k} \cos 3k\} = \frac{z(z - e^2 \cos 3)}{z^2 - 2z e^2 \cos 3 + e^4}$$

Review problems

6   Determine, using table 6.1, the z-transforms for a sampling period of 1 s of the samples taken of:
(a) $f(t) = t$, (b) $f(t) = te^{-2t}$, (c) $f(t) = \cos 3t$.

Table 6.1 z-transforms

	$f(t)$	$F(s)$	$f(k)$	$F(z)$
1	Unit impulse	1	$\delta(k)$	1
2	Unit step	$\dfrac{1}{s}$	$u(k)$	$\dfrac{z}{z-1}$
3	Unit ramp t	$\dfrac{1}{s^2}$	kT	$\dfrac{Tz}{(z-1)^2}$
4	t^2	$\dfrac{2}{s^3}$	$(kT)^2$	$\dfrac{T^2z(z+1)}{(z-1)^3}$
5	t^3	$\dfrac{6}{s^4}$	$(kT)^3$	$\dfrac{T^3z(z^2+4z+1)}{(z-1)^4}$
6	e^{-at}	$\dfrac{1}{s+a}$	$(e^{-aT})^k$	$\dfrac{z}{z-e^{-aT}}$
7	$1-e^{-at}$	$\dfrac{a}{s(s+a)}$	$1-(e^{-aT})^k$	$\dfrac{z(1-e^{-aT})}{(z-1)(z-e^{-aT})}$
8	te^{-at}	$\dfrac{1}{(s+a)^2}$	$kT(e^{-aT})^k$	$\dfrac{Tze^{-aT}}{(z-e^{-aT})^2}$
9	$(1-at)e^{-at}$	$\dfrac{s}{(s+a)^2}$	$(1-akT)(e^{-aT})^k$	$\dfrac{z[z-e^{-aT}(1+aT)]}{(z-e^{-aT})^2}$
10	$e^{-at}-e^{-bt}$	$\dfrac{b-a}{(s+a)(s+b)}$	$(e^{-aT})^k-(e^{-bT})^k$	$\dfrac{z(e^{-aT}-e^{-bT})}{(z-e^{-aT})(z-e^{-bT})}$
11	Item 6 with $e^{-aT}=c$		c^k	$\dfrac{z}{z-c}$
12	Item 8 with $e^{-aT}=c$		kTc^k	$\dfrac{kTz}{(z-c)^2}$
13	$\sin\omega t$	$\dfrac{\omega}{s^2+\omega^2}$	$\sin k\omega T$	$\dfrac{z\sin\omega T}{z^2-2z\cos\omega T+1}$
14	$\cos\omega t$	$\dfrac{s}{s^2+\omega^2}$	$\cos k\omega T$	$\dfrac{z(z-\cos\omega T)}{z^2-2z\cos\omega T+1}$
15	$e^{-at}\sin\omega t$	$\dfrac{\omega}{(s+a)^2+\omega^2}$	$(e^{-aT})^k\sin k\omega T$	$\dfrac{ze^{-aT}\sin\omega T}{z^2-2ze^{-aT}\cos\omega T+e^{-2aT}}$
16	$e^{-at}\cos\omega t$	$\dfrac{s+a}{(s+a)^2+\omega^2}$	$(e^{-aT})^k\sin k\omega T$	$\dfrac{z(z-e^{-aT}\cos\omega T)}{z^2-2ze^{-aT}\cos\omega T+e^{-2aT}}$
17	$\sinh\omega t$	$\dfrac{\omega}{s^2-\omega^2}$	$\sinh k\omega T$	$\dfrac{z\sinh\omega T}{z^2-2z\cosh\omega T+1}$
18	$\cosh\omega t$	$\dfrac{s}{s^2-\omega^2}$	$\cosh k\omega T$	$\dfrac{z(z-\cosh\omega T)}{z^2-2z\cosh\omega T+1}$

Note: T is the sampling period.

6.3.1 Laplace and z-transforms

It is quite common to have to determine the z-transform which corresponds with a particular Laplace transform. It should be noted that it is *not* obtained by simply substituting z for s. A basic approach that can be used is to determine the inverse Laplace transform, i.e. find $f(t)$, and then make the z-transformation. Some equivalent s- and z-transforms are given in table 6.1.

Example

Determine the z-transform for the sampled function for which

$$F(s) = \frac{1}{(s+a)(s+b)}$$

This Laplace transform can be looked up in table 6.1, item 10, to give the solution. Alternatively, by partial fractions the transform can be rearranged to give

$$F(s) = \frac{1}{b-a}\left[\frac{1}{s+a} - \frac{1}{s+b}\right]$$

Each of the terms can be looked up in table 6.1, item 6, to give the solution. Alternatively, we can work from the inverse Laplace transform, which is

$$f(t) = \frac{1}{b-a}(e^{-at} - e^{-bt})$$

Table 6.1, item 10, or the separate terms, item 6, can be used to obtain the solution. Alternatively, from the basic definition, i.e. equation [6], then

$$F(z) = \sum_{k=0}^{k=\infty} \frac{1}{b-a}(e^{-at} - e^{-bt})z^{-k}$$

$$= \frac{1}{b-a}[(1 + e^{-aT}z^{-1} + e^{-2aT}z^{-2} + ...)$$
$$- (1 + e^{-bT}z^{-1} + e^{-2bT}z^{-2} + ...)]$$

$$= \frac{1}{b-a}\left[\frac{1}{1 - e^{-aT}z^{-1}} - \frac{1}{1 - e^{-bT}z^{-1}}\right]$$

$$= \frac{1}{b-a}\left[\frac{z(e^{-aT} - e^{-bT})}{(z - e^{-aT})(z - e^{-bT})}\right]$$

The above example illustrates how different approaches can be used to obtain the solution.

Review problems

7   Determine the z-transforms for the sampled functions which have the Laplace transforms

$$\text{(a)} \ \frac{1}{(s+a)^2}, \ \text{(b)} \ \frac{s}{s^2+\omega^2}, \ \text{(c)} \ \frac{s+a}{(s+a)^2+b^2}$$

6.4 Properties of the z-transform

In this section basic properties of the z-transform are considered. Because of the relationship between the z and Laplace transforms, many of the properties of the Laplace transform are mirrored in those of the z-transform.

6.4.1 Linearity property

The z-transform of the sum of two sequences of samples corresponding to two time functions is the sum of the z-transforms of the two sequences when considered separately.

$$Z\{f(k) + g(k)\} = Z\{f(k)\} + Z\{g(k)\} \qquad [10]$$

Multiplication of the time function by a constant results in the multiplication of the z-transform by the same constant.

$$Z\{af(k)\} = aZ\{f(k)\} \qquad [11]$$

Example

What is the z-transform of the function $f(t) = t + e^{-t}$ when it is sampled every 1 s?

The z-transform of the sampled t term is given by item 3 in table 6.1 as

$$\frac{z}{(z-1)^2}$$

The z-transform of the sampled e^{-t} term is given by item 6 in table 6.1 as

$$\frac{z}{z-e^{-1}}$$

Hence the z-transform is

$$\frac{z}{(z-1)^2} + \frac{z}{z-e^{-1}}$$

Note that the sampled function could have been equally well written as $f(k) = k + e^{-k}$.

Review problems

8   What are the z-transforms of the following functions when sampled every 1 s:
(a) $f(t) = 2t$, (b) $f(t) = 10$, (c) $f(t) = t + 1$, (d) $f(t) = 2t + e^{-2t}$?

9   What are the z-transforms of the following sequences:
(a) $f(k) = 5k$, (b) $f(k) = 2k + e^{-k}$?

6.4.2 Time shift theorems

The *first shift theorem* can be written as: if $f(k)$ is a sequence and $F(z)$ its transform, then the z-transform of a sequence $f(k+n)$ is given by

$$Z\{f(k+n)\} = z^n F(z) - [z^n f(0) + z^{n-1} f(1)$$
$$+ z^{n-2} f(2) + ... + z f(n-1)] \qquad [12]$$

This theorem is concerned with shifts of a sampled sequence to the left. Thus suppose we have the sequence $f(k)$ of

0, 0, 0, 1, 1, 1, 1, ...

Then the sequence $f(k+1)$ would be

0, 0, 1, 1, 1, 1, 1, ...

and the sequence $f(k+2)$

0, 1, 1, 1, 1, 1, 1, ...

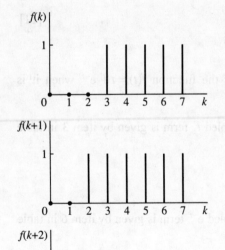

The above sequences are illustrated in figure 6.5. If the z-transform of $f(k)$ is $F(z)$ then that of the sequence $f(k+1)$ is

$$Z\{f(k+1)\} = zF(z) - zf(0)$$

and that of the sequence $f(k+2)$

$$Z\{f(k+2)\} = z^2 F(z) - [z^2 f(0) - zf(1)]$$

The *second shift theorem* can be written as: if the function $f(t)u(t)$ is shifted to the right by n sample intervals then the z-transform of the shifted sampled function is given by

Fig. 6.5 First shift theorem

$$Z\{f(k-n)u(k-n)\} = z^{-n} F(z) \qquad [13]$$

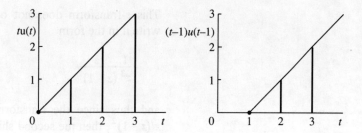

Fig. 6.6 Second shift theorem

where $F(z)$ is the z-transform of $f(k)$ which was the sampled sequence of $f(t)u(t)$. The second shift theorem is concerned with shifts to the right. To illustrate this, figure 6.6 shows the function $tu(t)$, and its sample $ku(k)$, and when shifted to the right to give the function $(t-1)u(t-1)$, and its sample $(k-1)u(k-1)$. Thus initially the sample was

0, 1, 2, 3, ...

and the shifted sample becomes

0, 0, 1, 2, ...

Example

Use table 6.1 to obtain the z-transform of the function $tu(t)$ when sampled at intervals of $T = 1$ s and hence obtain the transform of the sampled shifted function $(t-1)u(t-1)$. These are the functions illustrated in figure 6.6.

Table 6.1, item 3, gives the z-transform of the sampled function $tu(t)$ as

$$Z\{ku(k)\} = \frac{z}{(z-1)^2}$$

Hence, using the second shift theorem,

$$Z\{(k-1)u(k-1)\} = z^{-1}\frac{z}{(z-1)^2} = \frac{1}{(z-1)^2}$$

Example

What is the function which when sampled with a sample time of $T = 1$ s has a z-transform of

$$\frac{1}{z^2(z-1)^2}$$

This z-transform does not occur in table 6.1. However we can write it in the form

$$\frac{1}{z^3}\frac{z}{(z-1)^2}$$

and thus since the transform for the sampled function $tu(t)$ is $z/(z-1)^2$, then the second shift theorem indicates that the sampled function giving the transform is $(t-3)u(t-3)$.

Review problems

10 What are the z-transforms of the sequences
(a) $(k-3)u(k-3)$, (b) $u(k-2)$?
11 What is the z-transform of a unit step which has been shifted to start at $t = 2T$, where T is the sampling period?
12 What is the sequence which would give the following z-transform?

$$\frac{1}{z^3(z-1)}$$

6.4.3 Complex translation

The multiplication of $f(t)$ by the exponential e^{-at} requires the substitution of $z\,e^{aT}$ for z in the z-transform of the sample.

$$Z\{e^{-akT}f(k)\} = F(e^{aT}z) \tag{14}$$

Example

Determine, using the complex translation theorem, the z-transform of the sampled function $t\,e^{-at}$.

The z-transform of the sampled function t is given by table 6.1, item 3, as

$$\frac{Tz}{(z-1)^2}$$

The z-transform of the sampled $t\,e^{-at}$ is obtained by substituting $z\,e^{aT}$ for z, and so gives

$$\frac{Tz\,e^{aT}}{(z\,e^{aT}-1)^2} = \frac{Tz\,e^{-aT}}{(z-e^{-aT})^2}$$

Review problems

13 Use the complex translation theorem   to obtain the z-transforms of the sampled functions (a) $e^{-at}u(t)$, (b) $e^{-at}\sin\omega t$.

6.4.4 Final value theorem

The *final value theorem* gives the value that would be reached eventually by the sampled time function, i.e. the steady state sampled value. This theorem is

$$\lim_{t\to\infty}\ \{f^*(t)\} = \lim_{z\to1}\ \left\{\frac{z-1}{z}F(z)\right\} \qquad [15]$$

and applies subject to the condition that F(z) gives a sequence of terms that converges.

Example

What is the final value of the series which gives the following z-transform?

$$F(z) = \frac{z}{(z-0.1)(z-1)}$$

Applying the final value theorem, since when $t\to\infty$ we have $k\to\infty$,

$$\lim_{k\to\infty}\ \{f(k)\} = \lim_{z\to1}\ \left(\frac{z-1}{z}\right)F(z)$$

$$= \lim_{z\to1}\left[\frac{(z-1)z}{z(z-0.1)(z-1)}\right] = \frac{1}{0.9} = 1.11$$

Review problems

14 What are the final values of the sequences which have the following z-transforms?

(a) $F(z) = \dfrac{2z}{(z-1)(z^2 - 0.42z + 0.21)}$,

(b) $F(z) = \dfrac{0.5z^2}{(z-1)(z-0.2)(z-0.3)}$

6.4.5 Initial value theorem

The *initial value theorem* gives the value that the sampled time function has when $t = 0$. This theorem is

$$\lim_{t \to 0} f^*(t) = \lim_{z \to \infty} F(z)$$

and applies subject to the condition that such a limit exists.

6.5 The inverse z-transform

The sequence of samples represented by a z-transform, i.e. the inverse z-transform, can be obtained in a number of ways:

1. partial fractions,
2. long division,
3. the residue method.

Only the partial fractions and the long division methods are discussed in this book.

6.5.1 Partial fractions method

With this method the z-transform is expanded by partial fraction expansion into a sum of simple terms which can be recognised in terms of the standard z-transforms in table 6.1. Because virtually all the standard transforms have the term z in their numerators we generally work with $F(z)/z$ instead of just $F(z)$. The following example illustrates this.

Example

Determine the inverse transform of

$$F(z) = \frac{0.33z}{(z - e^{-0.4})(z - 1)}$$

Putting this in the form

$$\frac{F(z)}{z} = \frac{0.33}{(z - e^{-0.4})(z - 1)}$$

$$= \frac{A}{z - e^{-0.4}} + \frac{B}{z - 1}$$

Thus

$$A(z - 0.67) + B(z - 1) = 0.33$$

Putting $z = 0.67$ gives $B = -1$. Putting $z = 1$ gives $A = 1$. Thus

$$F(z) = \frac{z}{z - e^{-0.4}} - \frac{z}{z - 1}$$

Table 6.1, items 6 and 2, gives for the inverse transform the sequence

$$f(k) = e^{-0.4k} - 1$$

The sequence is thus

$$0, -0.33, -0.55, -0.70, ...$$

If there had been sampling time of $T = 1$ s then we could have written

$$F(z) = \frac{z}{z - e^{-0.4T}} - \frac{z}{z - 1}$$

and so

$$f(t) = e^{-0.4t}u(t) - u(t)$$

If there had been a sampling time of $T = 0.5$ s then we could have written

$$F(z) = \frac{z}{z - e^{-0.8T}} - \frac{z}{z - 1}$$

and so

$$f(t) = e^{-0.8T}u(t) - u(t)$$

The sequence of pulses is the same in each case but the function which generates them will depend on the sampling time used.

Review problems

15 Use the partial fraction method to determine the inverse z-transforms of the following:

(a) $F(z) = \dfrac{(1 - e^{-a})z}{(z - 1)(z - e^{-a})}$,

(b) $F(z) = \dfrac{z}{(z + 3)(z + 2)^2}$

6.5.2 Long division method

This method is probably best discussed by means of an example. Consider the z-transform

$$F(z) = \frac{2z}{z^2 + z + 1}$$

The procedure is to divide the numerator by the denominator using long division.

$$
\begin{array}{r}
2z^{-1} - 2z^{-2} + 2z^{-4} - 2z^{-5} + \dots \\
z^2 + z + 1 \overline{\smash{\big)}\, 2z} \\
\underline{2z + 2 + 2z^{-1}} \\
-2 - 2z^{-1} \\
\underline{-2 - 2z^{-1} - 2z^{-2}} \\
2z^{-2} \\
\underline{2z^{-2} + 2z^{-3} + 2z^{-4}} \\
-2z^{-3} - 2z^{-4} \\
\underline{-2z^{-3} - 2z^{-4} - 2z^{-5}} \\
2z^{-5}
\end{array}
$$

Thus we can represent $F(z)$ by a series, i.e.

$$F(z) = 2z^{-1} - 2z^{-2} + 2z^{-4} - 2z^{-5} + \dots$$

This is the transform of a sequence of impulses. We can thus write the sequence as

k	0	1	2	3	4	5 ...
$f(k)$	0	2	-2	0	2	-2 ...

A disadvantage of this technique is that only the sequence values are obtained.

Review problems

16 Using long division, find the inverse z-transforms in the form of the sample sequence for the following z-transforms:

$$\text{(a) } F(z) = \frac{5}{z+1}, \text{ (b) } F(z) = \frac{4z}{(z-1)^2}$$

Further problems

17 What are the samples produced for a sampling period of 0.5 s with the functions:
   (a) $f(t) = \sin 2\pi t$, (b) $f(t) = e^{-0.5t}$, (c) $f(t) = 2t^2$?

18 What are the sequences defined by:
   (a) $f(k) = k$, (b) $f(k) = 2$, (c) $f(k) = e^{-k}$?

19 Find the z-transforms of the following sequences with a sampling time of T:

(a) $f(0) = 1, f(1T) = 0, f(2T) = 0$, and all further values are 0.

(b) $f(0) = 0, f(1T) = 0, f(2T) = 2$, and all further values are 2.

(c) $f(0) = 0, f(1T) = 0, f(2T) = 1$, and all further values are 1.

20 What are the z-transforms of the following sequences?

(a) $f(k) = k$, (b) $f(k) = 2$, (c) $f(k) = e^{-2k}$, (d) $f(k) = 2\sin 3k$,

(e) $f(k) = 2 + e^{-3k}$, (f) $f(k) = e^{-2(k-3)}u(k-3)$,

(g) $f(k) = \sin 3k\, u(k) - \sin 3(k-4)\, u(k-4)$, (h) $f(k) = 3^k$.

21 What are the z-transforms of the signals with the following Laplace transforms, given that the sampling interval in each case is 0.1 s.

(a) $F(s) = \dfrac{5}{s^2 + 25}$, (b) $F(s) = \dfrac{6-s}{s(s+2)}$

22 Using partial fractions, find the inverse z-transforms of the following:

(a) $F(z) = \dfrac{z}{(z-1)(z-2)(z-3)}$,

(b) $F(z) = \dfrac{z(2z-1)}{(z-4)(z-5)}$,

(c) $F(z) = \dfrac{z^2}{z^2 - 3z + 2}$

23 Using long division, find the inverse z-transforms in the form of the sample sequence for the following:

(a) $F(z) = \dfrac{1}{z+1}$, (b) $F(z) = \dfrac{2z+1}{z^2+2}$, (c) $F(z) = \dfrac{2z^2-1}{z^2+4z+2}$

7 The z-transfer function

7.1 Discrete transfer function

As described in section 5.1, we can think of a block in a system as having a transfer function. This describes the relationship between the output and the input when an analogue signal is the input and an analogue signal is the output. In a similar way we can consider a block in a system when the input is digital and the output digital, hence a *digital transfer function* or *pulse transfer function*. We can use such transfer functions to describe the operation of blocks in such systems as digital control systems or digital filters.

The transfer function $G(s)$ describes the relationship between the output $Y(s)$ and the input $X(s)$ when both are in the s-domain, i.e. $G(s) = Y(s)/X(s)$. Thus if we take the z-transform of this equation we have

$$G(z) = \mathbb{Z}\{G(s)\} \tag{1}$$

The z-transfer function $G(z)$ of a discrete-data system can thus be defined as the ratio of the z-transform of the output $Y(z)$ to the z-transform of the input $X(z)$ when all initial conditions are zero.

$$G(z) = \frac{Y(z)}{X(z)} \tag{2}$$

$G(z)$ is referred to as the *digital transfer function* or the *pulse transfer function*.

Example

Determine the discrete transfer function for the electrical circuit shown in figure 7.1 when it has an input which is sampled at the rate of 10 Hz.

The Laplace transform of the components (see chapter 4) gives, when Kirchhoff's voltage law is applied,

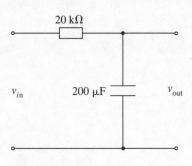

v_{in} 20 kΩ   200 μF v_{out}

Fig. 7.1 Example

110

$$RI(s) + \frac{1}{sC}I(s) = V_{in}(s)$$

Taking the output from across the capacitor, then

$$V_{out}(s) = \frac{1}{sC}I(s)$$

Thus, substituting into the earlier equation for $I(s)$ gives

$$RCsV_{out}(s) + V_{out}(s) = V_{in}(s)$$

Hence

$$G(s) = \frac{V_{out}(s)}{V_{in}(s)} = \frac{1}{RCs+1}$$

With the values given in the circuit diagram, then

$$G(s) = \frac{1}{4s+1} = \frac{0.25}{s+0.25}$$

The expression is of the form $a/(s + a)$. The z-transform of the transfer function gives, using item 6 in table 6.1,

$$G(z) = \frac{0.25z}{z - e^{-0.25T}}$$

With a sampling frequency of 10 Hz we have a sampling period T of 0.1 s. Thus

$$G(z) = \frac{0.25z}{z - 0.98}$$

Example

Determine the output response from a system with the following pulse transfer function when subject to a unit step input.

$$G(z) = \frac{1}{z-1}$$

The output $Y(z)$ in the z-domain is related to the input $X(z)$ by

$$Y(z) = G(z) \times X(z)$$

Hence, since for a unit step input we have

$$X(z) = \frac{z}{z-1}$$

then

$$Y(z) = \frac{1}{z-1} \times \frac{z}{z-1} = \frac{z}{z^2 - 2z + 1}$$

We can use long division to write this in terms for which we can easily obtain the inverse transformation. Thus

$$
\begin{array}{r}
z^{-1} + 2z^{-2} + 3z^{-3} + 4z^{-4} + \ldots \\
z^2 - 2z + 1\overline{\smash{\big)}\ z} \\
\underline{z - 2 + z^{-1}} \\
2 - z^{-1} \\
\underline{2 - 4z^{-1} + 2z^{-2}} \\
3z^{-1} - 2z^{-2} \\
\underline{3z^{-1} - 6z^{-2} - 3z^{-3}} \\
4z^{-2} + 3z^{-3}
\end{array}
$$

Thus we can represent $Y(z)$ by the series

$$Y(z) = z^{-1} + 2z^{-2} + 3z^{-3} + 4z^{-4} + \ldots$$

This is a transform of a sequence of impulses. We can thus write the output in terms of a sequence of pulses, at the sampling interval, of 1, 2, 3, 4, ... etc.

Review problems

1   Determine the pulse transfer function of systems which have transfer functions of

(a) $\dfrac{1}{s+4}$, (b) $\dfrac{4}{s(s+1)}$, (c) $\dfrac{1}{(s+1)(s+2)}$

2   Determine the output from a system with the following pulse transfer function when subject to a unit impulse input.

$$G(z) = \frac{1}{z+2}$$

7.1.1 Systems in series

Consider the situation where a sampled input to one system gives a digital output which is then fed into a second system as its input (figure 7.2). In the s-domain the overall transfer function is

$$G(s) = G_1(s) \times G_2(s)$$

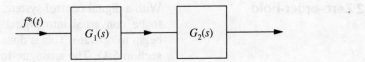

Fig. 7.2 Systems in series

Thus, the overall pulse transfer function is

$$G(z) = Z\{G_1(s) \times G_2(s)\}$$ [3]

The above equation represents a system where there is no further sampling occurring between the two systems but only prior to the first one.

Example

What is the overall pulse transfer function for a system consisting of two systems in series with transfer functions of $1/(s+1)$ and $10/(s+2)$?

We have to combine the two transfer functions in the s-domain and then obtain the z-transform of the resulting transfer function. Thus

$$G(s) = \frac{1}{s-1} \times \frac{10}{s-2} = \frac{10}{(s-1)(s-2)}$$

and the combined pulse transfer function is given by (item 10 in table 6.1)

$$G(z) = \frac{10z(e^{-T} - e^{-2T})}{(z - e^{-T})(z - e^{-2T})}$$

Note that we *cannot* take the z-transform of each component and multiply them together to give the resultant pulse transfer function.

Review problems

3   Determine the pulse transfer function of the following series systems when there is no sampler between the elements.

(a) $G_1(s) = 10$ and $G_2(s) = \dfrac{4}{s+2}$,

(b) $G_1(s) = \dfrac{2}{s}$ and $G_2(s) = \dfrac{1}{s+3}$,

(c) $G_1(s) = \dfrac{2}{s+2}$ and $G_2(s) = \dfrac{3}{s+3}$.

7.2 Zero-order-hold

With a digital control system, the analogue input to the system has to be converted into digital form before the control system can begin to operate. This is done by sampling the analogue signal (see section 6.1). The analogue-to-digital converter does however take a finite time to convert the sample into a digital signal and the sample has to be held at a constant value during this time. Thus the system invariably incorporates a *sample-and-hold* element which takes the sampled input and holds it constant for the time taken to convert the sample into a digital signal and become ready to take the next sample.

When a digital signal is converted into an analogue signal then a sample-and-hold element is generally used to hold the previously converted signal while the a new conversion takes place. The result is an analogue output signal which changes in a stepwise fashion.

One of the most common forms of a sample-and-hold element is the *zero-order-hold*. Figure 7.3 illustrates its action in

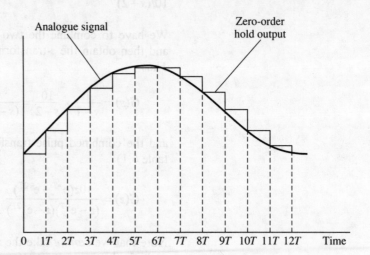

Fig. 7.3 Zero-order hold output

relation to an analogue-to-digital conversion. The signal is sampled and then held constant for the sampling period T. A unit impulse can thus be considered to give rise to a unit pulse of width T, as illustrated in figure 7.4(a). Such a unit pulse can be considered to be the sum of two unit steps, one occurring at time of $t = 0$ and the other delayed by a time T, i.e.

$$u(t) - u(t - T)$$

The Laplace transform of such a pulse is then

$$\frac{1}{s} - \frac{e^{-Ts}}{s} = \frac{1 - e^{-Ts}}{s}$$

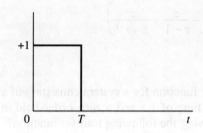

(a)

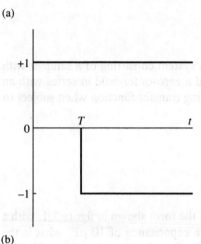

(b)

Fig. 7.4 A pulse as a sum of two steps

Since the input is a unit impulse with a Laplace transform of 1, then the transfer function of the zero-order-hold system is

$$G_{zoh}(s) = \frac{1 - e^{-Ts}}{s} \qquad [4]$$

In the analysis of a sampled-data system the transfer function of the zero-order-hold system must be taken into account. Thus the overall transfer function $G(s)$ of a system involving a zero-order-hold system in series with an element having a transfer function $G_1(s)$ is

$$G(s) = G_{zoh}(s) \times G_1(s)$$

$$= \frac{1 - e^{-Ts}}{s} G_1(s)$$

The pulse transfer function is then

$$G(z) = Z\left\{\frac{1 - e^{-Ts}}{s} G_1(s)\right\} \qquad [5]$$

Example

What is the pulse transfer function of a sampled-data system consisting of a zero-order-hold element in series with an element having the following transfer function?

$$\frac{1}{s(s + 1)}$$

The transfer function of the system will be

$$G(s) = \frac{1 - e^{-Ts}}{s} \times \frac{1}{s(s + 1)}$$

The discrete transfer function is given by taking the z-transform, i.e.

$$G(z) = Z\left\{\frac{1 - e^{-Ts}}{s^2(s + 1)}\right\}$$

Using partial fractions,

$$G(z) = Z\left\{(1 - e^{-Ts})\left(\frac{1}{s} - \frac{1}{s^2} + \frac{1}{s + 1}\right)\right\}$$

Multiplying in the s-domain by e^{-Ts} means a time shift of T (see section 1.6.3). Hence, using the second time shift theorem (section 6.4.2)

$$G(z) = \left(1 - \frac{1}{z}\right)\left(\frac{Tz}{(z-1)^2} - \frac{z}{z-1} + \frac{z}{z - e^{-1}}\right)$$

Review problems

4 What is the pulse transfer function for a system consisting of a sampler with a sampling time of 1 s and a zero-order-hold in series with an element having the following transfer function?

$$\frac{1}{s(s+2)}$$

5 What is the output from a system consisting of a sampler with a sampling time of 1 s and a zero-order-hold in series with an element having the following transfer function when subject to an impulse input?

$$\frac{1}{s(s+1)}$$

Further problems

6 For an electrical circuit of the form shown in figure 7.1, with a resistance of 25 kΩ and a capacitance of 10 μF, what is the pulse transfer function when there is a sampling time of 0.5 s?

7 For an electrical circuit of the form shown in figure 7.1 with a resistance of 1 Ω and a capacitance of 1 F, what is the pulse transfer function when there is a sampling time of 1 s?

8 Determine the pulse transfer functions of the systems produced by having two elements in series when they have the following transfer functions?

(a) $\frac{2}{s}$ and $\frac{4}{s+4}$,

(b) $\frac{1}{s+2}$ and $\frac{3}{s+3}$,

(c) $\frac{s}{s+1}$ and $\frac{1}{s+1}$

9 What is the pulse transfer function for a system consisting of a sampler with a sampling time of 0.5 s and a zero-order hold in series with an element having the transfer function 4/(s + 4)?

10 An open loop control system has an analogue input into an analogue-to-digital converter with a zero-order-hold element. The digital output is then operated on by a controller having a transfer function of 12/(s + 3). What is the digital transfer function of the system if the digital-to-analogue converter has a sampling time of 0.1 s?

11   A system consists of an analogue-to-digital converter with a zero-order-hold element feeding pulse signals with a sampling time of 0.5 s into a circuit consisting of a 25 kΩ resistor in series with a 10 µF capacitor. The output is the voltage across the capacitor. What is the pulse transfer function of the system?

12   A system consists of an analogue-to-digital converter with a zero-order-hold element feeding pulse signals with a sampling time of 1 s into a circuit consisting of a 1 Ω resistor in series with a 1 F capacitor. The output is the voltage across the capacitor. What is the pulse transfer function of the system?

13   A system consists of an analogue-to-digital converter with a zero-order-hold element feeding pulse signals every 1 s into an element with a transfer function of $1/(s^2 + s + 1)$. (a) What is the pulse transfer function of the system? (b) What is the output from the system for a unit step input?

14   A system consists of an analogue-to-digital converter with a zero-order-hold element feeding pulses every 0.5 s to an element with a transfer function of $1/[s(s + 2)]$. (a) What is the pulse transfer function of the system? (b) What is the output from the system for a unit impulse input?

15   An open loop control system consists of a sampler with a sampling time of 1 s and a zero-order-hold element in series with an element having a transfer function of $1/(s + 1)$. What is the response of the system to (a) a unit step input, (b) a unit ramp input?

Answers to problems

Chapter 1

1. $\dfrac{1}{s^2}$

2. $\dfrac{2}{s^3}$

3. $\dfrac{4}{s^2}$

4. $\dfrac{4}{s} + \dfrac{1}{s^2}$

5. (a) $5u(t)$, (b) $2u(t-3)$, (c) $3u(t-5)$

6. (a) $\dfrac{2}{s}$, (b) $\dfrac{3e^{-2s}}{s}$, (c) $\dfrac{5e^{-4s}}{s}$

7. $\dfrac{5\,e^{-4s}}{s}$

8. $\dfrac{e^{-4s}}{s}$

9. $4u(t-0.020) - 4u(t-0.035)$ V, $4\left[\dfrac{e^{-0.020s}}{s} - \dfrac{e^{-0.045s}}{s}\right]$ V

10. $10tu(t-1)$

11. $20u(t-1) - 20u(t-2)$

12. $\dfrac{e^{-2s}}{s^2}$, unit ramp starting at $t = 2$

13. (a) 2, (b) $2\,e^{-5s}$

14. Impulse of size 3 occurring at the delayed time of 2. $3\,e^{-2s}$

15. $5\delta(t-3)$

16. $2\delta(t) + 2\delta(t-0.02) + 2\delta(t-0.04) + 2\delta(t-0.06) + ...$

17. (a) $\dfrac{s}{s^2+\omega^2}$, (b) $\dfrac{a}{s(s+a)}$, (c) $\dfrac{120}{s^6}$, (d) $\dfrac{\omega^2}{s(s^2+\omega^2)}$

18. (a) $\dfrac{8}{s^2+16} - \dfrac{5s}{s^2+4}$, (b) $\dfrac{3}{s} + \dfrac{2}{s^2} - \dfrac{10}{s^3} + \dfrac{18}{s^4}$, (c) $\dfrac{5s}{s^2+16} - \dfrac{6}{s}$

19. $\dfrac{2}{s} + \dfrac{3}{s^2}$

20. $\dfrac{4}{s} + \dfrac{1}{s-2}$

21. (a) $\dfrac{12}{(s-2)^4}$, (b) $\dfrac{12}{(s+3)^2+16}$, (c) $\dfrac{2(s-4)}{(s-4)^2+4}$,

    (d) $\dfrac{3}{s-1} - \dfrac{3(s-1)}{(s-1)^2+1}$, (e) $\dfrac{2}{s-1} + \dfrac{2(s-1)}{(s-1)^2+1}$

22. $\dfrac{2e^{-2s}}{s^3}$

23. $\dfrac{2e^{-10s}}{s^2}$

24. $\dfrac{e^{-5s}}{s+3}$

25. $\dfrac{10}{1-e^{-2s}}\left(\dfrac{1}{s^2} - \dfrac{e^{-s}}{s^2} - \dfrac{e^{-2s}}{s^2}\right)$

26. $\dfrac{5(1-e^{-s})}{s(1+e^{-s})}$

27. (a) $\dfrac{\omega}{s^2+\omega^2}$, (b) $\dfrac{s}{s^2+\omega^2}$

28. (a) $10u(t)$ V, (b) $10u(t-2)$ V, (c) $4u(t-0.2) - 4u(t-0.3)$ V,
    (d) $4(t-1)u(t-1) - 4(t-3)u(t-3) - 8u(t-3)$ V

29. (a) $6\delta(t)$ V, (b) $6\delta(t-4)$ V,
    (c) $6\delta(t) + 6\delta(t-1) + 6\delta(t-2) + \dots$ V

30. (a) $\dfrac{5}{s}$ V, (b) $\dfrac{5e^{-3s}}{s}$ V, (c) $\dfrac{5}{s^2}$ V, (d) $\dfrac{5e^{-3s}}{s^2}$ V, (e) 5 V,

    (f) $5e^{-3s}$ V (g) $\dfrac{2\pi 50}{s^2+(2\pi 50)^2}$ V, (h) $\dfrac{2\pi 50\,e^{-3s}}{s^2+(2\pi 50)^2}$ V

31. (a) $\dfrac{1}{s+2}$, (b) $\dfrac{4}{s+2}$, (c) $\dfrac{8}{s(s+2)}$, (d) $\dfrac{5}{s} + \dfrac{8}{s(s+2)}$,

    (e) $\dfrac{1}{s} + \dfrac{2}{s^2} - \dfrac{3}{s^3}$, (f) $\dfrac{2}{s-2} - \dfrac{3}{s+3}$, (g) $\dfrac{8}{s^2+4} - \dfrac{3s}{s^2+4}$,

    (h) $\dfrac{3}{(s+2)^2+9}$, (i) $\dfrac{16}{s(s^2+16)}$

32. (a) $\dfrac{5/50}{s(s+1/50)}$ V, (b) $\dfrac{10}{s} + \dfrac{5/50}{s(s+1/50)}$ V, (c) $\dfrac{5}{s+1/50}$ V

33. (a) $\dfrac{1}{s} - \dfrac{e^{-3s}}{s}$, (b) $\dfrac{e^{-2s}}{s} - \dfrac{e^{-5s}}{s}$

34. (a) $\dfrac{e^{-2s}}{s^2}$, (b) $\dfrac{e^{-3s}}{s+1}$, (c) $\dfrac{2e^{-4s}}{s^2}$

35. $\dfrac{s\cos\theta - \omega\sin\theta}{s^2+\omega^2}$, $\dfrac{(s+a)\cos\theta - \omega\sin\theta}{(s+a)^2+\omega^2}$

36. $\dfrac{3(1-e^{-2s})}{s(1+e^{-2s})}$

37. $\dfrac{1}{s^2} - \dfrac{e^{-s}}{s(1-e^{-s})}$

38. $\dfrac{a}{s^2-a^2}, \dfrac{s}{s^2-a^2}$

39. (a) $\dfrac{s^3}{s^4+4a^4}$, (b) $\dfrac{a(s^2+2a^2)}{s^4+4a^4}$, (c) $\dfrac{a(s^2-2a^2)}{s^4+4a^4}$, (d) $\dfrac{2a^2s}{s^4+4a^4}$

Chapter 2

1. (a) $5\,e^{-10s}$, (b) $4t$, (c) $1-e^{-2t}$, (d) $2t^3$, (e) $3\,e^{2t}$, (f) $2\cosh 4t$,
    (g) $4\sin t$, (h) $\sin 2t$, (i) $4\cos 3t$, (j) $2\,e^{-2t}\cos 4t$, (k) $e^{2t}\sin 3t$,
    (l) $6\,e^{t}\sinh 3t$, (m) $e^{-t}\cos 2t$, (n) $e^{-3t}\cos 2t$

2. (a) $2t+2t^2$, (b) $\cos 3t-3\sin 3t$, (c) $\cos 2t-3\sin 2t$,
    (d) $4t+\tfrac{1}{3}t^3$

3. (a) $\dfrac{3}{s+1}-\dfrac{2}{s-2}$, (b) $-\dfrac{1}{6s}+\dfrac{3}{10(s-2)}-\dfrac{2}{15(s+3)}$,
    (c) $\dfrac{5}{s+4}-\dfrac{2}{s+2}$, (d) $\dfrac{3(1-s)}{2(s^2+1)}+\dfrac{3}{2(s-1)}$,
    (e) $\dfrac{2}{(s-1)^2}-\dfrac{1}{s-1}+\dfrac{1}{s+1}$, (f) $5-\dfrac{15}{s+4}+\dfrac{5}{s-2}$

4. (a) $\dfrac{e^{-at}-e^{-bt}}{b-a}$, (b) $4\cos 4t+\sin 4t$, (c) $\dfrac{1}{4}+\dfrac{11e^{-4t}}{4}$,
    (d) $2\,e^{t}+4\,e^{-3t}$, (e) $3\,e^{-3t}-8\,e^{-2t}+5\,e^{-t}$, (f) $-e^{3t}+5e^{t}$
    (g) $2+3e^{3t}-3e^{-3t}$

5. (a) $e^{-2t}t^2$, (b) $3\,e^{2t}t^2$, (c) $2\,e^{-2t}\sin 4t$, (d) $e^{2t}+4t\,e^{2t}$

6. (a) $\cos[3(t-2)]u(t-2)$, (b) $\sin[3(t-3)]u(t-3)$,
    (c) $(t-2)u(t-2)$

7. (a) $\tfrac{1}{4}(1-\cos 2t)$, (b) $\sin t-t\cos t$, (c) $4(e^{3t}-e^{-t})$

8. (a) $5\,e^{-10t}$, (b) $10t$, (c) $2(1-e^{-3t})$, (d) $e^{-4t}-e^{-5t}$, (e) $\sin 4t$,
    (f) $e^{2t}t^3$, (g) $2\cos 4t$, (h) $e^{-25t}+15t\,e^{-25t}$, (i) $(1-t)\,e^{-t}$,
    (j) $e^{3t}-\cos 2t-\sin 2t$, (k) $4\,e^{-t}+6\,e^{2t}$,
    (l) $10\,e^{-t}-16\,e^{-2t}+6\,e^{-3t}$, (m) $2(t-5)\,e^{-2(t-5)}u(t-5)$,
    (n) $(t-3)^3\,e^{2(t-3)}u(t-3)$, (o) $3t+t^2-\cos 3t+3\sin 3t$,
    (p) $2\,e^{-4t}+16\cos 4t$, (q) $\tfrac{1}{24}t^4-6\sin 2t$,
    (r) $2\cos 2t-\tfrac{5}{2}\sin 2t-e^{4t/3}$

Chapter 3

1. See text
2. (a) $3[sX(s)-4]+2X(s)$, (b) $2[sX(s)-2]+X(s)$
3. See text
4. (a) $[s^2+2s+2]X(s)-4s-7$, (b) $[2s^2-3s+1]X(s)-4s+8$

5. $\dfrac{3}{s\left[(s+2)^2+9\right]}$

6. $\left[Ls+R+\dfrac{1}{Cs}\right]I(s)$

7. (a) $x = 0.4(1 - e^{-5t})$, (b) $x = 2.5(1 - e^{-2t/3})$

8. $i = \dfrac{V}{R}(1 - e^{-Rt/L})$

9. (a) $x = \frac{2}{3}\left[t - \frac{4}{3}(1 - e^{-3t/4})\right]$, (b) $x = 3(e^{2t} - e^{-t/2})$,

   (c) $x = e^{-t} + \frac{1}{3}t^3 e^{-t}$

10. (a) $x = 2e^{-t} - 2e^{-3t}$, (b) $x = 5e^{-t} - 5e^{-2t} + 2e^{-3t}$,

    (c) $x = 2e^{2t} + e^{-t}$, (d) $x = -\frac{1}{2} + \frac{1}{3}e^{4t} - \frac{1}{6}e^{-2t}$,

    (e) $x = \frac{1}{25}(54e^{-2t} + 105te^{-2t} - 4\cos t + 3\sin t)$

11. $x = 10\cos 2t$

12. $x = 10e^{-2t} + 20te^{-2t}$

13. (a) $x = 5e^{-t} + 3e^{4t}$, $y = 5e^{-t} - 2e^{4t}$,

    (b) $x = \frac{2}{7}(e^{2t} - e^{-5t})$, $y = \frac{1}{7}(e^{2t} + 6e^{-5t})$,

    (c) $x = \frac{1}{2}(2 - e^{-2t/3} + e^{-2t})$, $y = \frac{1}{2}(e^{-2t} - e^{-2t/3})$,

    (d) $x = \frac{1}{10}(5 - 3e^{-6t/11} - 2e^{-t})$, $y = \frac{1}{5}(e^{-t} - e^{-6t/11})$

14. (a) 0, (b) 4

15. As text

16. (a) 0, (b) 1

17. (a) $x = 2e^t - 1$, (b) $x = \frac{1}{2}(5e^t - t - 1)$,

    (c) $x = 2e^{3t} - 2\cos 2t - 3\sin 2t$, (d) $x = \frac{1}{4}(e^{-4t} + 1)$,

    (e) $x = \frac{1}{17}(4\cos t + \sin t - 4e^{-4t})$

18. (a) $x = \frac{1}{17}[(4\cos 2t + 2\sin 2t)e^{-t} + \sin 2t + 4\cos 2t]$,

    (b) $x = 3(\sin t - te^{-2t})$, (c) $x = (t - 1)e^{-t} + e^{-2t}$,

    (d) $x = 1 + e^{-2t}\sin t$, (e) $x = (1 + 4t)e^{-2t}$

19. (a) $x = \frac{1}{2}(e^{-t} + e^{-3t})$, $y = \frac{1}{2}(e^{-3t} - e^{-t})$, (b) $x = e^t + e^{-t}$,

    $y = e^{-t} - e^t + \sin t$, (c) $x = \frac{3}{5} + \frac{1}{6}e^t - \frac{3}{4}e^{-t} - \frac{1}{60}e^{-5t}$,

    $y = \frac{2}{5} + \frac{1}{3}e^t - \frac{3}{4}e^{-t} + \frac{1}{60}e^{-5t}$

20. $i = 40te^{-400t}$

21. $i = \dfrac{V}{R}(1 - e^{-Rt/L})$

22. $i = \frac{1}{2}(e^{-t} + \sin t - \cos t)$

23. $i = \dfrac{2}{R}[1 - e^{-R(t-5)/L}]u(t - 5)$

24. $q = 10[1 - e^{-4t}]u(t)$

25. $q = 10[1 - e^{-4(t-3)}]u(t-3)$

26. $q = \frac{1}{5\sqrt{3}} e^{-5t} \sin 5\sqrt{3}\, t$

27. $x = 3\cos 4t + 4\sin 4t$

28. $x = \left[\frac{1}{2} - e^{-(t-1)} + \frac{1}{2} e^{-2(t-1)}\right] u(t-1)$

29. (a) 3, 0, (b) 5, 10

30. As text

31. As text

32. 1, 2

33. 0, 0

34. 2, 3

Chapter 4

1. Series: $0.050s\ \Omega$, -10 mV s; parallel: $0.050\ \Omega$, $0.2/s$ A s

2. Series: $0.01s\ \Omega$, $2\ \mu$V s; parallel: $0.01s\ \Omega$, $2/s$ mA s

3. Series: $0.5 \times 10^{-6}s\ \Omega$, $5/s$ V s; parallel: $0.5 \times 10^{-6}s\ \Omega$, $-2.5\ \mu$A s

4. (a) $60\ \Omega$, (b) $10 + 0.002s\ \Omega$, (c) $10 + \dfrac{1}{8 \times 10^{-6}s}\ \Omega$, (d) $\dfrac{20}{3}\ \Omega$,

   (e) $\dfrac{0.02s}{10 + 0.002s}\ \Omega$, (f) $\dfrac{10}{1 + 80 \times 10^{-6}s}\ \Omega$

5. (a) $\dfrac{0.5s + 20}{10s}$ S, (b) $\dfrac{0.5 \times 10^{-5}s^2 + 1}{0.5s}$ S

6. $2 + \dfrac{3}{s+2}$ V

7. $0.5 + \dfrac{2}{s}$ V

8. $i = 4e^{-2t}$ A

9. $i = 4e^{-2t}$ A

10. $i = \dfrac{v\omega}{R^2 + \omega^2 L^2}\left[L e^{-Rt/L} - L\cos\omega t + \dfrac{R}{\omega}\sin\omega t\right]$

11. $i = \dfrac{20}{2 \times 10^{-5} - 1} e^{-t}\sin(2 \times 10^{-5} - 1)t$ A

12. $i = CV(1 - e^{-t/CR})$

13. $i = 2e^{-3t}\sin 4t$ A

14. $i = \frac{4}{11}(1 - e^{-55t/2})$ A

15. $i = 2[1 - (1+t)e^{-2t}]$ A

16. (a) $1\ k\Omega$, (b) $0.5s\ \Omega$, (c) $1/(2 \times 10^{-6}s)\ \Omega$

17. (a) $100 + 0.01s\ \Omega$, (b) $1000 + 1/10^{-5}s\ \Omega$,

    (c) $1000 + 0.01s + 1/10^{-5}s\ \Omega$, (d) $s/(100 + 0.01s)\ \Omega$,

    (e) $10^{-5}s/(1 + 10^{-7}s^2)\ \Omega$

18. $i = 0.1(1 - e^{-20t})$ A

19. $v = 2 - 1.5 e^{-t/4}$ V

20. $v = 6(1 - e^{-10t})$ V

21. $i = \frac{1}{25}(5 - 2 e^{-3t})$ A

22. $i = kC - \dfrac{kL}{R^2} + \dfrac{kt}{R} + \dfrac{kL}{R^2} e^{-Rt/L}$ A

23. $i = 0.63 e^{-t} \sin 31.6t$ A

24. $v = 30 - 40 e^{-1000t} + 10 e^{-4000t}$ V

25. $i = 0.005 e^{-1000t}$ A

26. $i = 0.01 \sin 2000t$ A

27. $i = 5 \times 10^{-3}(1 + 3 e^{-5000t})$ A

28. $i = -0.017 e^{-400000t} + 0.017 \cos 10^6 t + 0.043 \sin 10^6 t$ A

29. $i = t e^{-t}$ A

30. $i = 8 e^{-11t} \cos 10t - 7.2 e^{-11t} \sin 10t$ A

Chapter 5

1. $\dfrac{1}{As + \rho g/R}$

2. (a) $G[t - \tau(1 - e^{-t/\tau})]$, (b) $G\dfrac{1}{\tau} e^{-t/\tau}$

3. (a) 30 s, (b) 7.5×10^{-4} V, (c) 1.8×10^{-4} V

4. $\dfrac{3}{s^2 + 4s + 5}$

5. Underdamped

6. $b_0[1 - 1.19 e^{-4t} \sin(9.2t + 66.4°)]$

7. $\dfrac{K}{9}(t - 2 e^{-3t} + t e^{-3t})$

8. $12 e^{-2t} - 9 e^{-3t} - 3 e^{-t}$

9. $\dfrac{k}{(Ls + R)(Is + c)}$

10. $\dfrac{2}{s^2 - 1}$

11. $\dfrac{5}{s + 53}$

12. $\dfrac{5s}{s^2 + s + 10}$

13. $\dfrac{2}{3s + 1}$

14. $\dfrac{2}{1 - s}$

15. $\dfrac{k}{(Ls + R)(Is + c) + kK}$

16. 0.25

17. (a) Zero -4, poles -1 and -2, (b) no zeros, poles 0 and -1,
    (c) zero -3, poles $+1 \pm j2$, (d) zero 0, poles $-2 \pm j1$

18. (a) Unstable, (b) stable, (c) stable, (d) unstable, (e) unstable,
    (f) critically stable, (g) stable

19. (a) $\dfrac{1}{ms^2 + cs + k}$, (b) $\dfrac{1}{R + 1/Cs}$, (c) $\dfrac{1}{LCs^2 + RCs + 1}$

20. (a) $\dfrac{1}{RCs + 1}$, (b) $\dfrac{R_2 C_2 s + 1}{(R_1 + R_2)C_2 s + 1}$,
    (c) $\dfrac{s(L_2 C_2 s + R_2 C_2)}{L_2 C_2 s^2 + (R_1 + R_2)C_2 s + 1}$

21. (a) 3 s, (b) 0.67 s

22. (a) $1 + e^{-2t}$, (b) $2 + 2 e^{-5t}$

23. (a) Overdamped, (b) underdamped, (c) critically damped,
    (d) underdamped

24. $t e^{-3t}$

25. $2 e^{-4t} - 2 e^{-3t}$

26. 0.2, 5 rad/s

27. $\sqrt{10}$

28. $\theta = 2.02 e^{-0.2t} \sin 1.98t$

29. (a) $\dfrac{4s}{s^2(s + 1) + 1}$, (b) $\dfrac{2(s + 2)}{s^2 + 3s + 4}$, (c) $\dfrac{4}{s^2 + 5s + 1}$,
    (d) $\dfrac{2}{s^2 + 2s + 10}$

30. 49

31. (a) Zero $+ 1$, poles $+ 3, + 2$; (b) zero $0, -1$, poles $-1, +1, +2$,
    (c) zero $+\frac{1}{2}$, poles $0, -2$, (d) zeros none, poles $-1 \pm j1.4$

32. (a) Critically stable, (b) unstable, (c) stable, (d) stable,
    (e) stable

33. 23.5

34. 0.5

35. $\dfrac{3}{(s + 3)(s + 1)}$, stable

36. R/L, c/I

Chapter 6

1. (a) 1, 2, 4, 8, 16, ..., (b) 1, 3, 5, 7, ...,

    (c) 1, 0.37, 0.14, 0.05, ...

2. 0, 0, 0, 1, 1, 1, ...

3. $e^{-0.05k}u(k)$

4. (a) $\dfrac{z}{z-e^{-aT}}$, (b) $\dfrac{z}{z-2^{T}}$, (c) $\dfrac{3Tz}{(z-1)^{2}}$, (d) $\dfrac{10z}{z-1}$,

    (e) $\dfrac{10z}{z-1}+\dfrac{3Tz}{(z-1)^{2}}$

5. (a) $\dfrac{1}{z(z+1)}$, (b) $\dfrac{3z}{(z-1)^{2}}$

6. (a) $\dfrac{z}{(z-1)^{2}}$, (b) $\dfrac{z\,e^{-2}}{(z-e^{-2})^{2}}$, (c) $\dfrac{z(z-\cos 3)}{z^{2}2z\cos 3+1}$

7. (a) $\dfrac{Tz\,e^{-aT}}{(z-e^{-aT})^{2}}$, (b) $\dfrac{z(z-\cos \omega T)}{z^{2}-2z\cos \omega T+1}$,

    (c) $\dfrac{z(z-e^{-aT}\cos bT)}{z^{2}-2z\,e^{-aT}\cos bT+e^{-2aT}}$

8. (a) $\dfrac{2z}{(z-1)^{2}}$, (b) $\dfrac{10z}{z-1}$, (c) $\dfrac{z}{(z-1)^{2}}+\dfrac{z}{z-1}$,

    (d) $\dfrac{2z}{(z-1)^{2}}+\dfrac{z}{z-e^{-2}}$

9. (a) $\dfrac{5z}{(z-1)^{2}}$, (b) $\dfrac{2z}{(z-1)^{2}}+\dfrac{z}{z-e^{-1}}$

10. (a) $\dfrac{1}{z^{2}(z-1)^{2}}$, (b) $\dfrac{1}{z(z-1)}$

11. $\dfrac{1}{z(z-1)}$

12. $(k-4)u(k-4)$

13. (a) $\dfrac{z}{z-e^{-aT}}$, (b) $\dfrac{z\,e^{-aT}\sin \omega T}{z^{2}-2z\,e^{-aT}\cos \omega T+e^{-2aT}}$

14. (a) 2.53, (b) 0.89

15. (a) $f(k)=1-e^{-ak}$, (b) $f(k)=1-(-3)^{-k}$

16. (a) 0, −5, +5, −5, ..., (b) 0, 0, 4, 8, 12, 16, ...

17. (a) 0, 0, 0, ..., (b) 0, 0.78, 0.61, 0.22, ...,(c) 0, 0.5, 2, 4.5, ...

18. (a) 0, 1, 2, 3, ..., (b) 2, 2, 2, 2, 2, ..., (c) 1, 0.37, 0.14, ...

19. (a) 1, (b) $\dfrac{2z}{z^{2}(z-1)}$, (c) $\dfrac{Tz}{(z-1)^{2}}$

20. (a) $\dfrac{z}{(z-1)^{2}}$, (b) $\dfrac{2z}{z-1}$, (c) $\dfrac{z}{z-e^{-2}}$, (d) $\dfrac{2\sin 2}{z^{2}-2z\cos 2+1}$,

    (e) $\dfrac{2z}{z-1}+\dfrac{z}{z-e^{-3}}$, (f) $z^{-3}\left(\dfrac{z}{z-e^{-2}}\right)$, (g) $\dfrac{(1-2z^{-4})z\sin 3}{z^{2}-2z\cos 3+1}$,

    (h) $\dfrac{z}{z-3}$

21. (a) $\dfrac{z\sin 0.5}{z^2 - 2z\cos 0.5 + 1}$, (b) $\dfrac{3z}{z-1} - \dfrac{4z}{z - e^{-0.2}}$

22. (a) $0.5 - 2 \times 2^k + 1.5 \times 3^k$, (b) $5^k + (-4)^k$, (c) $2 \times 2^k - 1$

23. (a) $0, 1, -1, 1, -1, ...$, (b) $0, 2, -1, -4, 2, ...$,

    (c) $2, -8, 27, -92, ...$

Chapter 7

1. (a) $\dfrac{z}{z - e^{4T}}$, (b) $\dfrac{4z(1 - e^{-T})}{(z-1)(z - e^{-T})}$, (c) $\dfrac{z(e^{-T} - e^{-2T})}{(z - e^{-T})(z - e^{-2T})}$

2. $+1, \ -2, \ +4, \ -8, ...$

3. (a) $\dfrac{40z}{z - e^{-2T}}$, (b) $\dfrac{2z(1 - e^{-3T})}{3(z-1)(z - e^{-3T})}$, (c) $\dfrac{6z(e^{-2T} - e^{-3T})}{(z - e^{-2T})(z - e^{-3T})}$

4. $\dfrac{1}{4}\left(\dfrac{2}{z-1} - \dfrac{1 - e^{-2}}{z - e^{-2}}\right)$

5. $0, 0.37, 0.77, 0.91, ...$

6. $\dfrac{4z}{z - e^{-2}}$

7. $\dfrac{z}{z - e^{-1}}$

8. (a) $\dfrac{2z(1 - e^{-4T})}{(z-1)(z - e^{-4T})}$, (b) $\dfrac{3z(e^{-2T} - e^{-3T})}{(z - e^{-2T})(z - e^{-3T})}$,

    (c) $\dfrac{z[z - e^{-T}(1 + T)]}{(z - e^{-T})^2}$

9. $\dfrac{1 - e^{-2}}{z - e^{-2}}$

10. $4(1 - z^{-1})\left(\dfrac{z}{z-1} - \dfrac{z}{z - e^{-0.3}}\right)$

11. $\dfrac{1 - e^{-2}}{z - e^{-2}}$

12. $\dfrac{1 - e^{-1}}{z - e^{-1}}$

13. (a) $\dfrac{0.34z + 0.24}{z^2 - 0.79z + 0.37}$, (b) $0.34, 0.85, 1.12, 1.15, ...$

14. (a) $\dfrac{0.092z + 0.066}{(z-1)(z - 0.37)}$, (b) $0.092, 0.192, 0.229, ...$

15. (a) $0.63, 0.86, 0.95, 0.98, 1, 1, 1, ...$,

    (b) $0.63, 1.50, 2.45, 3.43, 4.40, ...$

Index

admittance in s-domain 56, 62

capacitor in s-domain 59
circuits 56
  admittance 56, 62
  C 59
  elements in s-domain 56
  ideal sources 63
  impedance 56, 62
  in s-domain 61
  Kirchhoff's laws 61
  L 57
  mesh analysis 68
  node analysis 68
  R 56
  RC 42, 43, 64
  RCL 66
  RL 40, 65
  time constant 42
closed loop system 81
complex frequency domain 6
convolution theorem 33

derivatives, transforms 35
differential equations
  first order 41
  second order 45
  simultaneous 46
  solving 40
Dirac-delta function 10

feedback systems 80
final value theorem 50, 105
first shifting property 16, 102

gain 73

heat transfer 43

Heaviside function 5

impedance in s-domain 56, 62
impulse function, defined 9
inductor in s-domain 57
initial value theorem 49
integrals, transforms 38
inverse transform 23, 106

Kirchhoff's laws in s-domain 61

Laplace transform
  convolution 33
  defined 2
  derivatives 35
  final value theorem 50
  initial value theorem 49
  integrals 38
  inverse 23
  operator 2
  properties 14
  table 12
  z-transform 100
linear system 74
linearity 14, 23, 101

mass–spring system 40
mesh analysis 68

node analysis 68

partial fractions 25, 106
periodic functions 19
poles 82

rectified sine wave 19
resistor in s-domain 56

sampled data systems 92
s-domain 1
  shifting property 16, 31
second shift theorem 17, 102
simultaneous differential equations 46
stability 83

time constant 42
time domain 1, 2
  shifting property 6, 17, 32
transfer function 73
  digital 110
  discrete 110
  feedback systems 80
  first-order system 74
  pulse 110
  second-order system 76
  series systems 79, 112

unit impulse function 10
unit ramp function 4
unit step function 4, 5, 7

window function 6

zero-order hold 114
zeros 82
z-transform
  complex translation 104
  defined 95
  final value theorem 105
  first shift theorem 102
  inverse 106
  Laplace transform 100
  properties 101
  second shift theorem 102
  standard 98
  table 99